THE HEALER OF SHILLONG

REVEREND DR HUGH GORDON ROBERTS AND THE WELSH MISSION HOSPITAL

by Dr D. Ben Rees

MODERN WELSH PUBLICATIONS

First published in Great Britain March 2016

Copyright 2016 by D. Ben Rees

The moral right of the author has been asserted.

All profits from the sale of this book will be donated to the
Dr Gordon Roberts Hospital, Shillong Appeal.

This volume is dedicated to the memory of his successor at Shillong
Hospital, Dr Arthur Hughes.

Printed in Malta by Melita Press and published by Modern Welsh
Publications, of Allerton, Liverpool

ISBN 0 901332 96 8

Modern Welsh Publications
www.welshpublications.co.uk

CONTENTS

INTRODUCTION

Whilst on a visit to Shillong, in the Khasi-Jaintia Hills, in North East India, in November 2012, I was overwhelmed by the high esteem and love that the local people have for the Presbyterian Church of Wales (or the Calvinistic Methodist Church of Wales), even amongst the young people. The reason for this was the rich inheritance which had been passed from generation to generation due to the pioneering work of Welsh men and women who had responded to God's call to extend His kingdom beyond the borders of Wales. Other denominations had been spreading the Christian Gospel in parts of India by the time that Thomas Jones arrived in Cherrapunji in 1841. Thomas Jones immediately addressed one urgent need. Due to neighbouring tribes invading the area over the centuries a written language did not exist. However, with the help of local people who had a good knowledge of the English language Thomas Jones created an alphabet which led to a written language and, subsequently, to education.

Another apparent need was medicine. H. Gordon Roberts qualified as a Bachelor of Medicine and Surgery in 1912 and the following year both he and his wife Catherine (nee Jones), offered themselves as medical missionaries, and, as reported in this biography they left for Shillong at the end of 1913, regarding this as God's calling.

Following the decision to build a new hospital Dr Roberts shouldered most of the responsibilities, facing many difficulties, which are detailed in this volume. Since its commissioning in 1922, the hospital has increased from 90 beds to 350 beds.

The Dr H. Gordon Roberts Hospital in Shillong celebrates its century of medical service in 2022. The hospital's Governing Board led by Dr David Tariang has embarked on a project to address many of the present day challenges which faces the medical ministry of the Presbyterian Church of India. The development will benefit the whole of Meghalaya state; a new Centenary Building is being built on the present hospital land and will provide a custom built theatre suite and wards for Children's surgery, Orthopaedic and Urological Surgery, radiological diagnostic facilities together with space for expanding new specialities. Although very ambitious the project will not only improve facilities which have become cramped and outdated but will also recognise the pioneering work of Dr H. Gordon Roberts and his successors. The hospital, formerly known as the Welsh Mission Hospital, has since 1967, been run by the Presbyterian Church of North-East India. The motto of the hospital is, 'In His Name to heal, to teach and to preach.'

The Presbyterian Church of Wales is regarded by the Khasi-Jaintia people as the mother church and at the 2014 General Assembly the PCW launched The Moderator's Appeal giving its members an opportunity to support the venture, both in prayer and donations. Some of the proceeds of this volume will go towards the Appeal.

In this volume, The Reverend Doctor D. Ben Rees provides a truly valuable biography of one in a long list of Welsh men and women to whom generations of the Khasi-Jaintia Hills people are so indebted; likewise we are indebted to Dr Rees for chronicling the contribution of one of our own people in a far off land.

Rev. Trefor Lewis (Moderator of the Presbyterian Church of Wales 2013-2014)

PREFACE

This volume is being published to fill a gap in the history of Welsh Presbyterian missionaries to India. Reverend Dr H. Gordon Roberts achieved a great deal. He established a Hospital in Shillong which in 2022 will be celebrating its centenary. I had written a short entry on him in the book I edited in 2002 called Vehicles of Grace & Hope published by the William Carey Library. At last I have prepared a substantial study of his sacrifice, determination, leadership with regard to the building of a Hospital in the town of Shillong. I was also inspired by the efforts of my fellow Presbyterians to raise funds for the H. Gordon Hospital in Shillong as they have exciting plans for their centenary. All the proceeds from this book will be consecrated to the Hospital.

I have been involved in the North India – Wales Trust from its inception and I am proud of all our efforts. This book is part of the publishing agenda of the Trust. I am grateful for the Introduction by Reverend Trefor Lewis which captures the atmosphere. His call to action is commendable. My friend Dr John G. Williams of Liverpool has read the typescript and offered a number of useful insights to strengthen the story. Another outstanding medical man, Mr Gwyn A. Evans, Weston Rhyn, near Oswestry who has served in his retirement the Hospital in Shillong has also read the text. I am grateful to Mrs Bethan Richards, Swansea for the photographs which add to the story. She has provided photos of Dr Gordon Roberts himself which we treasure. These photographs as well as the photographs that came from the collection of the National Library of Wales add immensely to our historical account. Let us then appreciate Dr Roberts and his staff in Shillong. I call him the Healer of Shillong, an appropriate title.

D. Ben Rees, Liverpool, 1 October 2015

Miss Morgan.   Rev. Rai Bhajur.   Dr. E. Williams.   Rev. J. C. Evans.   Miss Evans.

Miss L. Jones.   Mrs. E. Williams.   Mrs. Evans.   Miss Reid.

Miss E.M. Lloyd

Miss Lillian Jones and Miss Laura Evans

Present day Hospital in Shillong

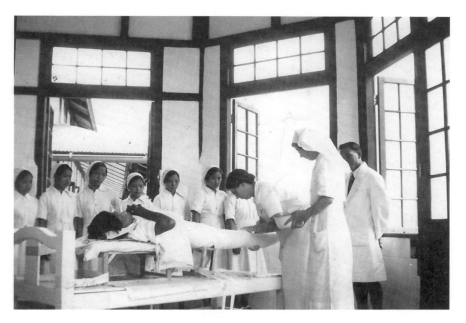

Early nursing in the Welsh Mission Hospital

Revd Richard Lumley of Wallasey,
a supporter of the Medical Mission work

Reverend J.D.Evans, minister of Catharine Street Chapel, Liverpool and mentor of Gordon Roberts and his wife

Revd Joseph Jenkins,
revivalist and an influence on Gordon Roberts

Dr H. Gordon Roberts and Mrs. Nancy Williams

Mrs. Nancy Williams as a patient

Dr Gordon Roberts and his co-workers in the mission field

BACKGROUND

Liverpool was the centre of the Welsh Presbyterian Missionary organisation in North East India from 1840 to 1970. The failure of Liverpool born Josiah Hughes to go to India as a missionary in 1830 was the first mistake of the domineering London Missionary Society. They refused others to go ten years later including Thomas Jones who had been a student in the recently opened College at Bala. The father of Josiah Hughes, an elder in Liverpool, was not at all pleased and

Thomas Jones (1810-1849)

this was true of a number of his friends, including a few ordained men of God. So this was the catalyst for a number of Welsh Calvinistic Methodists led by John Hughes, Mansfield Street in the growing town of Liverpool to hold a public meeting at Rose Place Welsh chapel on 31 January 1840 to consider the possibility of setting up an independent society from the autocratic London Missionary society. They took the plunge. It was not easy. But they had a cause near to their hearts. Before the end of 1840 Thomas Jones and his wife sailed from the

Parch. Josiah Thomas, M.A., Liverpool.

Liverpool docks to Calcutta as their first official missionaries. It was a long journey but they made it. Most of the organisation to support Thomas Jones and the future missionaries took place in the city (town until 1880) and its officers, in particular the General Secretary shouldered a great deal of responsibility for the welfare of missionaries in Assam and North East India. A delightful hymn writer and a native of Liverpool Reverend John Roberts (Minimus, 1808- 1880) was the first holder of the office, but he did it on a voluntary basis for twenty six years without a salary.

When he resigned in 1866 the work was undertaken on a full-time salary by the Reverend Josiah Thomas (1830-1905), who had three other exceptional brothers namely Dr Owen Thomas, Dr John Thomas and William Thomas, a temperance campaigner. They all ministered in Victorian Liverpool. It was a disappointment to the missionary witness when Josiah Thomas took a well-deserved retirement in 1900, but his successor for the next 31 years was the Reverend Robert John Williams (1857-1933), whose son Glyn served as an Elder in the Welsh Presbyterian Church at Heathfield Road, near Penny Lane.

During the early part of my ministry, Glyn Williams often told me of his father's commitment to the Foreign Mission. RJ Williams accomplished a great deal. The National Library of Wales holds a large number of his letters and they indicate his care for the work in India and how glad he was to see young men from Liverpool responding to the need. He was absolutely thrilled when a talented lad living in the city called Hugh Gordon Roberts expressed an interest in missionary work.

He was not alone among those employed in the missionary office in Falkner Street near the Philharmonic Hall; for it was not easy to find dedicated medical men who were willing to venture to Assam.

Hugh Gordon Roberts was born on 16 July 1885 in Liverpool, England, the son of David Roberts, a much respected elder in Catherine Street Presbyterian Church of Wales or as it was known in those days the Calvinistic Methodist Church. His wife Jane Sarah Roberts, was the daughter of Thomas and Mary Jones both of them from Liverpool.[1] Gordon Roberts inherited the larger portion of his father's character and commitment to the Welsh Presbyterian denomination. On his father's side, the family came from from the farmstead of Mynydd-y-Gof on the outskirts of Holyhead on the island of Anglesey, where the Dr David Roberts (1788-1869), Gordon's great-grandfather practiced the skills of medicine.[2] Dr David Roberts had eight sons and each one of them achieved a great deal of stardom in the world of medicine, religion, commerce and civic affairs. The third of these brothers, Thomas Foulkes Roberts who lived in Llanidloes in Montgomeryshire, was Gordon's grandfather.[3]

The grandson was educated privately and then entered the prestigious and private educational establishment called Liverpool College, where he did well. On leaving Liverpool College he was articled to a firm of chartered accountants where he would have remained most probably for the rest of his career had it not been for the Religious Revival at the turn of the twentieth century. The young Welsh revivalist, Evan Roberts, travelled to Liverpool to conduct a campaign in April 1905 during the Welsh Religious Revival at the invitation

of Reverend John Williams, minister of the large Welsh-speaking
Princes Road Calvinistic Methodist Chapel, in Toxteth as well as the
Liverpool Welsh Free Church Council.[4] Gordon Roberts heard the
evangelist preach on the text 'How shall we escape if we neglect so
great a salvation?' and was converted in the fervour of the 1904-6
Welsh Religious Revival. His devout parents were naturally delighted
at his religious commitment and encouraged him to consider for a career
the family tradition of medicine. Without any hesitation he enrolled as
a student in the Faculty of Medicine at the University of Liverpool
where he qualified in the spring of 1912 as a Bachelor of Medicine
and Bachelor of Surgery[5] Dr H. G. Roberts after qualification was
appointed a house surgeon in the Shaw Street Women's Hospital
situated in Islington, Liverpool.

He became engaged to Miss Catherine (Katie) Jones, who belonged
to the same church, and through the guidance of their minister, Revd
J.D. Evans and the Student Christian Movement of the University
of Liverpool, they both considered the call for missionaries to North
East India, where their denomination had had a mission field since
Thomas Jones and his wife Anne went out in 1840.[6] In March 1913,
Dr H. G. Roberts offered himself to the Reverend R. J. Williams and
the General Purposes Committee that met in their office in 16 Falkner
Street, Liverpool.[7] In April he was accepted by the Mission Committee
and on 16 May it was decided to ask the North Wales Association
of the Presbyterian Church of Wales if they would ordain him to the
missionary field in India[8] Gordon Roberts and Katie Jones married
in the summer of 1913 before leaving for India. He was ordained as a

Minister of Religion in accordance with the denomination's emphasis on evangelisation as the main priority, much more important in their eyes in those days than the medical work. Medicine came second, in their opinion, to the task of salvation of souls.[9] A farewell meeting was held for him and his wife in their Catherine Street Presbyterian Church (which has long been demolished) on 15 October 1913 and they sailed a few days later for Calcutta, and then the long difficult route to the Khasi Jaintia Hills.

THE EXPECTATIONS IN THE KHASI-JAINTIA HILLS

As soon as the Welsh Presbyterian missionaries on the Khasi Jaintia Hills heard that the Revd Dr Hugh Gordon Roberts had been accepted for missionary service they met to decide where he should be stationed. They first asked the Government to approve the building of a hospital in Shillong and had received a disapproving reply –
"There was already a dispensary in Shillong which met all the needs".[10]

Therefore they began to review two or three possible sites outside Shillong in the direction of Cherrapunji. On 5 September 1913 their committee decided, after some very complicated strategic voting, that the hospital should be sited on the plateau above Shillong, six to eight miles outside the town and that in the meantime Reverend Dr Gordon Roberts should look after the spiritual needs of the Mawphlang District, an area which seemed to be about a quarter of the size of Wales.[11]

THE IDEAS OF THE LIVERPOOL-BASED MISSIONARY COMMITTEE

The Mission committee in Liverpool also began, in a more leisurely manner, to consider the siting of the hospital. It first of all decided that the decision should be left until Dr Roberts reached Shillong, but then out of the blue some two days after Dr Roberts' farewell meeting in Liverpool it came to the decision that the hospital should be in Shillong itself.[12] The committee soon began to draw up rough plans for the hospital, for the consideration of the Welsh Presbyterian missionaries there on the Khasi Hills. The intention now was that Dr Gordon Roberts should start the work of building a hospital as soon as possible.

Writing on 18 November, 1914, soon after his arrival in Shillong, Dr Roberts wrote to the General Secretary Revd R.J.Williams that Shillong itself would appear to him to be far the best place for the new hospital building. He added a very strong practical point : *'I understand that crowds of people from a radius of about thirty miles come into the market in Shillong, once or twice a week and would find it more convenient if the hospital were in town rather than outside it.'*[13] He also informed the General Secretary, Rev. R.J. Williams that – *"he urgently wanted drugs"* and requested the office in Liverpool to ask Evans Lescher and Webb to supply as they would for the White Star ships carrying 1000 passengers for eight weeks, in accordance with the Board of Trade scale, to do the same for him.[14] Concerning the site, he was now urging caution, which suited his paymasters in the Liverpool office. At all costs he wanted to avoid precipitancy, *"for considerations of the water supply; the best position; the extent of the site; room for expansion; had all to be thought of"*.[15]

In the meantime he had seen some of the countryside of the Khasi Hills and seemed to be impressed with the idea favoured by the traditionalists that there should be religious activities there, and that they were to be seen to be done in the name of Welsh Presbyterianism, outside the community as soon as possible. Reverend Dr John Roberts (1842-1908), the Principal of the Theological college in Cherrapunji led his fellow missionaries, and believed strongly that every medical missionary should have some churches under his care.[16] His influence lasted for years as Dr Gordon Roberts soon realised. Dr Gordon Roberts toyed with the idea of acquiring a motorbike and sidecar so that he could go up and down the badly designed main roads of the Khasi-Jaintia territory to see patients at appointed places, but he also saw the advantages of a small medical centre in a convenient place.

WELCOME TO DOCTOR ROBERTS AND HIS BELOVED WIFE

Over Christmas and New Year he had been extremely busy at Cherrapunji and a number of his fellow Welsh missionaries were ready to co-operate. J.Ceredig Evans, E.H.Williams , John M.Harries-Rees were authorised to start the collecting of materials. They were the backbone of the Building Committeee for the new Hospital.

Dr Gordon Roberts regarded the three of them as his dependable lieutenants. [17]

In the District Committee in Laitkynsew which met on 24 February, 1914, the Welsh missionaries gave an official welcome to Dr and Mrs Robert and expressed it in a diplomatic manner:

"We are glad that we have now to welcome a medical man that is so fully qualified and equipped by special training for carrying on the work according to the latest scientific principles and at the same time is so full of missionary spirit that we look forward to much blessing on their department of mission works."[18]

At the same District Committee they came to a final conclusion about the site for the new hospital. This was to be on a hill on the north western side of Shillong called Jaiaw, the spot on which the West Walian Rev Ceredig Evans lived before the earthquake in 1897 which destroyed all the buildings on the Hills belonging to the Welsh Mission [19]

Dr Roberts submitted a scheme for the New Hospital to cost 45,000 rupees, (worth £10,500 today) including equipment. He expected Rs 25,000 from the Government, and he expected the Mission Committee in Liverpool to provide Rs 20,000, of which Rs 12,000 had already been collected. A local building committee in Shillong had already been appointed to look over the plans.

In the Treasury (the English monthly magazine for the Presbyterian Church of Wales) of August 1913 there is the statement –
"Dr Gordon Roberts is going out to Shillong to take charge of a New Hospital which is to be built there...there is no money in hand for the New Hospital at Shillong, but our English Churches will see to it, that having provided such excellent workers, that some share of the expense will also be forthcoming".[20]

This invitation to the English language churches within the Presbyterian Church of Wales, was made with the fullest understanding by the committee that no special appeal would be permitted – spontaneous gifts by interested friends was all that was sanctioned by the Liverpool based directors.

This statement was made before Dr H. Gordon Roberts had left Liverpool and he would consequently have gone out to Shillong without any assurance that there was money ready to use to build the hospital. It would therefore be very heartening to him that the Rev John Ceredig Evans (1855-1936) could tell him in the District Committee that in the Earthquake Fund there was a certain sum especially given to defray the cost of rebuilding the Cherra Hospital. This money he now naturally hoped to claim. Ceredig Evans was a highly influential figure, an Inspector of Schools, a long serving missionary, and an effective representative on the Assam Legislative Council and his word meant a great deal.

A NEW APPROACH TO GOVERNMENT

The grounds of the new appeal to Government were couched as follows:

1. That the Welsh Mission Hospital was for the whole of the Khasi Hills.

2. That the Khasi people who had been converted to Christianity by Welsh Presbyterian missionaries were very reluctant to enter any secular hospital called a Government Hospital.

3. That the Welsh Mission needed a hospital of its own to which it could send its chapel members and others from all parts of the Hills for healing.

4. That the Mission could not train compounders properly unless it had a hospital (compounders were a cadre of men or women trained to compound medicines and dress wounds, equivalent perhaps to the medical assistants in the Third World projects of the present day, some of them might also undertake midwifery).

There is no further reference to compounders in all the subsequent history of the hospital, for none were ever trained there. Two of the earlier Welsh medical missionaries, Dr Edward Williams (1866-1925) a native of Corwen and his colleague Dr Griffith Griffiths (1852- 1922), a native of the Lleyn peninsula, had always trained compounders and had given elementary training to many teachers and pastors in their pastorates.[21]

To this appeal the Government replied, (5 May 1914), *"that from their point of view the present Government Dispensary was quite sufficient for the medical needs of the place, but from our point of view he could now quite see that it was not."* The Government spokesman then said that the Welsh Presbyterians fully deserved support and that they would like to give them a substantial grant, but that they had very little money to spare for medical work. They could manage to scrape together Rs 5000, – the smallness of this grant aid was a considerable financial setback to Dr Roberts' hopes.[22]

While all this was going on Dr Roberts' new house was being built, close by the house which he and Mrs Roberts currently occupied. At least there was some positive action happening.

DR ROBERTS BECOMES A CIVIL SURGEON

The Great War had begun and India's military medical services were being called up to serve. Major Scott of the Indian Medical Service, the Civil Surgeon to the Khasi Jaintia Hills, was also called up in due course and Dr Gordon Roberts was asked by Government to act in his place.[23] The Welsh Mission authorities agreed that he should give the desired assistance. Dr Roberts remained as a Mission servant and continued to receive the Mission salary. The payment that Government gave for his services, according to the standing rules of the Mission, would be handed over to the Mission. But the missionary did not abide with the rules laid down. He ignored them and Dr Roberts paid the Government salary into an account which he used to help to fund the New Hospital project. It was a brilliant move on his behalf but completely out of order if it happened anywhere else within the Presbyterian Church of Wales.

THE BUILDING OF THE NEW HOSPITAL - JANUARY 1915

Revd Dr Gordon Roberts started to build as soon as he could, in fact in the winter of 1915. He felt and indeed expected that it would be cheaper to start immediately, for inflation and the shortage of materials was already being experienced.

Dr Roberts bought Major Scott's car when he left for military service and began his official work as Civil Surgeon. The Mission had granted him £70 to buy a car and he was allowed to pay the rest out of his earnings as Civil Surgeon.[24]

He now attended the Civil Dispensary and he also saw patients at his own small Mission Dispensary. He also saw private patients and members of the Civil Service at their own homes. Since the outbreak of the First World War, many European families in Calcutta and the Plains who would have otherwise returned to England were unable to secure passages, so they came instead to Shillong to escape the heat of the Plains. This additional influx of Europeans added greatly to Dr Roberts' work and to his ability to increase his hospital building fund.

THE FIRST MAJOR ABDOMINAL OPERATION

Two months after he became Civil Surgeon he performed his first major abdominal operation on a Khasi patient namely a caesarean section. It is impossible to say if this was the first caesarean section ever to have been performed in Shillong, (it may well have been the first Caesarean section ever done by Dr Roberts!), but it was the first of many that he performed, and mother and baby did well.

He reported at that time that he arranged for all the worst cases to see him at the Civil Hospital; poor as they might be, the facilities there were better than in his own mission dispensary. Nevertheless he could say *"Cases are coming to me as the missionary and not as the Civil Surgeon"*.[25]

Miss Beatrice Jones, the daughter of the fervent evangelist Rev John Jones of Jowai, was the nurse in the Civil Hospital. As Ednyfed Thomas said of John Jones, *"It is certain that the most evident witness to the devotion and godliness was that as many as five of his children became missionaries."* Beatrice Jones' presence enabled Dr Roberts to carry out his surgery.[26] It is important to emphasise at this stage that Dr Roberts' achievements in surgery were possible because of the assistance of nurses like Beatrice Jones whom he could trust. He was of that generation of medical graduates which produced the general practitioner surgeons who were responsible for much of the surgery done in many parts of Britain for the next twenty or thirty years. Many areas in Wales were totally dependent on the services of such men, who, never having had the opportunity to work with the specialist surgeons of the major medical centres for any prolonged period, yet faced the challenges of surgical emergencies and performed various services to their communities with flying colours.

It was in these days that Dr Roberts first set out a claim form for a sister for the New Hospital, believing that it would be unwise to leave a large Mission hospital without a nurse[27]. By September 1915, with Dr Roberts supervising the progress of the building in his spare time, much of the building of the first part of the hospital had been completed. Experiencing the major part of his first monsoon in India taught him what the rains could do to buildings and property. This caused him to send out his first plea for more funds, to build verandas to shield the windows and for covered ways between the wards. He also wanted to replace plaster with stone for better sturdiness in monsoon weather, *'and money to build accommodation for relatives to stay near their patients.'* He was at this time keeping close to tradition.

By January 1917 he had to report to the Mission General Secretary, Revd R. J. Williams, that he had long since used up all the Mission grant plus the equipment grant and the Government grant and that he was now using up the money he earned as Civil Surgeon while still in the Mission employ[28] Williams was not too pleased but he was wise enough to steer away from a confrontation. Dr Roberts tried his best to have a short furlough in 1917 but the directors would not budge on this. It was suicide to try and come back in the middle of the hostilities and he had not completed his allotted period of service to the Lord. Dr

Roberts could be at times difficult to deal with. It proved a tug of war between the Liverpool based Office and him throughout the year.[29]

By the end of 1918 he had come to an arrangement with the Office in Liverpool that he should resign from the Welsh Mission to enter Government employ.[30] This decision enabled him to come back to his family in Liverpool. This would never have happened to him if he was under the jurisdiction of the Missionary Office and Committee - the Welsh Presbyterian Mission would have required him to complete seven years' service to qualify for leave unless he had serious medical grounds to receive a furlough. It also enabled him to go home at Government expense with a bonus of Rs 2000 in lieu of leave. Since he had now finished three years as Civil Surgeon and the First World War was over, the Government would release him and pay his passage home.

But even during his furlough, he was eagerly looking forward to return to Shillong, so as to get back to the Welsh Mission work untrammelled by Government business.

A FINAL STATEMENT

He now gave a final statement – (the first of many final statements) – as to what had been accomplished:
* The New Hospital Main building was now complete at the cost of about Rs 75000 (say at least £17,000 in 2015), against an estimate

of Rs 45000.

- Mission had contributed Rs 350000 (say £2,333)
- Government had contributed Rs 5000 (say £333)
- He himself from Civil Surgeon earnings, Rs 30000 (£2000)

But he would still need about Rs 50,000. This sum was to pay for an isolation ward, out-buildings, electric supply and to complete the huge sanitation system.

He hoped that when he reached Liverpool he would be able to collect more money, and that he wouldn't be considered too ambitious in his vision.

"I am convinced after five years in this country that I am a missionary first and a doctor afterwards. I would like sanction to build a new bungalow."

This new bungalow had been the subject of many unsuccessful appeals. This bungalow was needed for him to live literally next door to the hospital instead of half a mile away up the hill. It would, he said:

"1. Increase patient confidence who came to stay in the hospital. This would save time and money. It would also facilitate emergency calls.

2. The present bungalow was too far away – it was at least half a mile uphill.

3. The present bungalow was within a few yards of the Girls' school hostel and would be good if the ladies in charge of educational work occupied this. Their present bungalow in any case was too small for two people".

The Welsh Presbyterian Mission Committee based in Liverpool would not give permission to build the bungalow until after he had returned to the field, but it did approve of the suggestion that he should now approach the Government again for a grant.[31]

Dr Roberts was now in a much stronger position to plead for a grant. He knew all the important people. The Inspector General of Civil Hospitals of Assam gave him a glowing inspection report after visiting the empty hospital building and so did Major General Cree from Delhi, representing the Military authorities. Here follows a copy of a letter sent by Dr Gordon Roberts to the Second Secretary serving the Chief Commissioner of Assam in February 1919 (through the Inspector General of Civil Hospitals Assam).[32]

Dear Sir,
I have the honour to approach you with reference to the New Mission Hospital, Shillong.

I.   The Main Building has at last been erected at the cost of
                                                    Rs 70,000

This amount has been provided as follows:
(a)   From the Directors of the Welsh Mission   Rs 35,000
(b)   Special contribution from the Government of Assam
                                                    Rs 5,000
(c)   Special contribution made by myself from my earnings as Civil

Surgeon, Shillong   Rs 30,000
                                                         Rs 70,000

This building (which is fitted throughout with hot and cold water supply) contains the following rooms:

A.   Waiting room
     Consulting room
     Examination room
     Eye room
     Medicine or compounding room
B.   Laboratory
     X-ray room
C.   Modern operating theatre with anaesthetic and sterilising rooms attached
D.   Two large surgical wards (male and female)
     Two large medical wards (ditto)
E.   Eight private wards
F.   Office rooms for nurses and doctors
G.   Eight bathrooms (with latrines attached)

Apart from the above it will be necessary to erect two bungalows; one for European nurses, and the other for myself. The cost of these, which will be about Rs 24,000, will be met by the Welsh Calvinistic Methodist Mission authorities. It will be readily recognised that the best work can be done only when doctors and nurses live in close proximity to the hospital. For this reason it is essential that the new bungalows be built as soon as possible.

II.   (a) It will be readily recognised that the installation of X-Ray and electric light is a necessity and not a luxury. After careful consideration and consultation with experts I am of opinion that a private electric plant would be the most suitable provision.

(b) The provision of a septic tank is also most desirable on public health grounds. It may be noted that such provision has been made at St Edmund's College, Pine Mount School and elsewhere. It will enable us to supply sanitary flushing latrines both inside the building and outside.

III.   The outbuildings will include: Assistants quarters, Compounders and assistant nurses quarters, several segregation wards, kitchens, mortuary, etc. These are all essential to the running of the hospital.

IV.   It may perhaps be permissible for me to point out that in erecting a large mission hospital we do not suggest that the present Government Civil Hospital is not sufficient for the needs of Shillong. Our aim is directed rather toward meeting the needs of the numerous villages throughout the whole length and breadth of the Khasi Hills. The very large majority of these villagers are simple and unsophisticated and have a very real dread of submitting themselves to treatment, either as out-patients or in-patients of a Government Hospital. I admit that their unwillingness to seek the medical aid provided for them may be very unreasonable, but such is the case. On the other hand I would point out that the Welsh Mission has been working on these hills for over seventy years, with the result that the missionaries have, through frequent touring in the interior, to a great extent won the confidence of the people, non-Christian as well as Christians. I can state from personal observations and enquiry that there are innumerable cases needing medical and surgical assistance which remain untreated and all too often succumb after months or years of suffering. Careful enquiries in many directions have convinced me that the New Mission Hospital, Shillong, will meet a very real need.

I propose to keep in touch with the whole Khasi Hills and to pay visits to Cherra, Mawphlang and many other places, my knowledge of the Khasi language will be of considerable assistance in this connection and by constant advertisement of the existence of the hospital will unquestionably have a beneficial effect upon the health of the community. Not being burdened by any official or administrative duties, I hope to be free to give my whole time to this work.

It is proposed that two, if not three or more European nurses will form part of the staff of the New Hospital.

V.   In approaching you thus through the Inspector General of Civil Hospitals, I do so, not simply because this is the proper channel through which to send my application, but also because he is well acquainted with my plans. He has taken the very greatest interest in my work and I therefore bring the matter up through him with full confidence that he will readily appreciate all that I have represented. On various occasions the Inspector General paid visits of inspection to the Main Building of the hospital and made most valuable suggestions in connection with the building generally – particularly concerning the operation theatre, the dressing rooms and the wards. I am extremely grateful to him for his unfailing kindness on the different occasions on which I sought his help and advice.

VI.   Finally may I again draw your attention to the financial position. The Welsh Mission is by no means wealthy. In giving Rs 35,000 towards the Main Building they have done more almost than they can afford. As may be well imagined the War has seriously impoverished many of the Mission subscribers. Personally, I have done my best in giving the Rs 30,000 of my own money. Sir Arundale Earle in his inspection note on the main building expressed his regret that Government had only given the small sum of Rs 5,000 towards the costs and hoped that, after the conclusion of hostilities, a much larger amount would be given.

I have pointed out that the Mission will be called upon to erect the two bungalows at the cost of about Rs 25,000. I will have to prevail upon the Mission to provide this amount.

The total contribution by the Mission (already given or to be given), will be as follows:

Towards the cost of the Main Building   – Rs 35,000
Cost of erecting two bungalows   – Rs 25,000
Cost of equipment of Main building (part of which – Rs 15,000 is invested in War Loan)
By personal contribution to the cost of the Main   – Rs 30,000
     – Rs 105,000

May I therefore earnestly ask the Government of Assam to be so good as to defray the cost of Electric light and X-ray, septic tank, and out-buildings, the cost of which will amount to Rs 60,000.

I have the honour to be sir your most obedient servant,

H. Gordon Roberts

In due course a letter came from Sir Beatson Bell, the Chief

Commissioner of Assam:

"We should give the whole Rs 60,000, if only to mark our appreciation of Dr Roberts' work. To offer any smaller sum would savour of meanness and ingratitude. As much as possible should be given this year".[33]

Dr Roberts was able to inform the Liverpool General Committee on 16 April 1919:

"No outhouses have hitherto been arranged for, but Government has just granted Rs 60,000 for this purpose. This sum was allocated as follows:

Out buildings	– Rs 25,000
Electricity costs	– Rs 25,000
Septic tank	– Rs 10,000

A quid pro quo was inserted in the conditions of the grant, (namely to provide X-ray and electro-medical services free and in perpetuity to Government servants) for these buildings was sent by Dr Gordon Roberts to the Directors and they were approved in the following terms:

"The Committee wished to express its heartfelt thanks to Dr Roberts for his generosity in putting so large a part of his personal earnings for the purpose. We realise also that the Government grant of Rs 60,000 is a direct result of Dr Roberts' work as a Civil Surgeon.

The Chairman proposed that we declare our great appreciation of Dr Roberts' service and his incomparable generosity in connection with the hopital".[34]

It was a huge psychological victory for Dr Roberts.

DR GORDON ROBERTS RETURNS TO LIVERPOOL HAVING ACCOMPLISHED GREAT THINGS

Revd Dr H. Gordon Roberts once expressed the hope that when he returned to his home city on leave he would be able to collect more money for the project. He was not given leave for this special appeal – at least not at the first endeavour, but he was allowed to publish a pamphlet for interested friends who would be likely to help. This was the expression of the settled principle not to allow special appeals as distinct from campaigns to further the purposes of the General Fund which was for evangelisation.

In the event the Connexion, which had not supported a special appeal since the Earthquake Fund of 1897, was swept off its feet by a great campaign which attained the status of a national cause. It resulted in the establishment of a fund of the order of £30,000 for the Shillong Hospital.[35] Possibly the awakening of the churches to responsibilities outside their own country as expressions of compassion, like the *"Save the Children Fund"* in the aftermath of the Great War, accounted in part for the tremendous success of the appeal.

After all, the destructiveness and horror of the Great War was there for all to see. This was a glad response to an appeal for something in shining contrast to all the starkness and tragedy of the past four years.

Dr and Mrs Roberts went out to Shillong in 1913 with the kindly and half romantic view of them as two young people going out to the unknown of the Mission Field: Dr Roberts with the reputation generously ascribed to all young doctors when they engage upon their first practice, and Mrs Roberts, as the charming shy young lady who was to be his helpmate and support in a strange land.

DR ROBERTS HAD COME BACK IN A COMPLETELY DIFFERENT GUISE

He had built a hospital during wartime (admittedly not yet ready for habitation). He was a man of action. He had shown a dedication to that purpose and a capacity for self-financing which had enabled him, while still a Mission servant, to use the salary emoluments to further the building programme. He was willing to sacrifice. He had funded that building with a considerable contribution from his own earnings in the second phase of his appointment as Civil Surgeon. His zeal and example had disposed Government officials to acknowledge his great service to them during the War and they had made a very generous grant to complete the building of the hospital in Shillong.

He had demonstrably retained his missionary evangelistic zeal – he was *"still first of all a missionary and then a doctor"* and he could write:

"The hospital will be of incalculable value in helping us to reach the hearts of the people. Our one great passion and desire is to lead on to Christ and the hospital is all very secondary to this. Will you ask the friends to pray for us that we may be emptied of self and live only for Christ. The work is great and we are so weak. Will you pray that we may be made strong in the Master's service."[36]

His mentor Revd J. D. Evans, ably assisted by Revd Watcyn Pryce, arranged a series of missionary exhibitions and large meetings for Dr Roberts all over Wales and Merseyside to share his vision of the hospital.[37.] But during his well-earned furlough Dr Roberts stamped his authority on the directors of the Welsh Presbyterian Church Foreign Mission. He could hold his own on every front and in every meeting that was arranged in the office at 16 Falkner Street, Liverpool. On the strategy of evangelism and on financial affairs to do with the hospital, he was able to give the details and provide a full answer to every question. As a medical practitioner he was gaining expertise and knowledge which endeared him to the directors. The result of all this was truly remarkable, a total of £30,000 was received for the new Mission Hospital in Shillong. He was truly a man of God with the vision of a medical evangelist. Dr Gordon Roberts and his supportive wife returned to Shillong in November 1920 and he was invited to serve as a nominated member of the Chief Commission of the Legislative Council for the Province. Then on 11 April 1921, he was invited to Government House, where he was presented with the Kaiser-Hind (Gold) Medal for services to the community. Life was hectic. He was practising as a medical director as well as acting as

Clerk of Works for the new hospital.

Building continued on both new buildings – the outbuildings, the isolation ward; the sanitary system; the bungalows and, to his great distress, the repair or replacement work involved because of the ravages of white ants. This picture frequently reappeared in Dr Roberts' prayers and sermons as a dire warning to all lest sin should quietly and unseen eat away the Christian character. Sin involved great cost, the price of forgiveness. Often he was on the verge of breakdown, but he kept going with enthusiasm for the furtherance of the Gospel.

THE FIRST MISSIONARY NURSING SISTER ARRIVES TO HELP

Miss Margaret Buckley, a nursing sister from South Wales, had first come out to Shillong in October 1919.[38] During Dr Roberts' absence on furlough in Wales she worked in the Civil Hospital. When Dr Roberts returned she joined him in the New Hospital building and was very actively involved in preparations to welcome patients.[39] She also began to attract girls to help her at this work and to begin training them as professional nurses. Dr Roberts began to see outpatients there quite soon after his return from Liverpool and Wales, but his time was largely taken up with the supervision of the building and his public responsibilities. Despite expressing the hope in April 1921 that they would soon be able to take inpatients, it was not until shortly before the official opening of the hospital on March 25, 1922, that any inpatients were actually admitted. It may be that he still operated occasionally at the Civil Hospital for he describes *"interesting"* cases in his letters.

The stresses of these days must have been considerable for first one nurse then the other became ill. Indeed, Miss Buckley herself had to be operated upon for appendicitis.[40] She was the first patient to be operated upon in the hospital. Dr Edward Williams came from Jowai, a journey of thirty miles on horseback, to give the anaesthetic, and Major Scott, the Civil Surgeon assisted. Miss Margaret Buckley, so it is said, prepared the theatre herself.

At this time Dr Roberts' letters to the General Secretary in Liverpool described a pretty dire situation, he himself on the point of breaking down and Miss Buckley carrying on when she ought to have been resting in bed.[41] The Secretary expressed great concern and recommended that he should not try to have all the buildings put up at once, urging him rather to take things as easily as he could. He reduced his medical commitments, but he started to write propaganda letters home appealing for nurses, letters described by the Rev J Hughes Morris as too long to be included in the missionary magazine, but he did get one published in Welsh Outlook on the necessity of the medical work to combat demon worship.[42]

In December 1921 he was much concerned with the installation of electricity and the setting up of the sanitary system. This was very costly because the men who installed both systems were brought up from Calcutta. He was also much concerned about the cost of installing the sanitary system, but he could not defer the buildings because this would have necessitated bringing the men up from Calcutta twice, a journey by rail and road that would take some thirty hours.

This project, the provision of modern sanitation, although it was not the first to use a water carriage system in Shillong, was certainly the largest and most sophisticated system in the town - possibly in the whole of Assam - and it ushered in the dawn of new methods in dealing with hospital sanitation in the Province. It became no longer necessary to have *"everything"* carried in a bucket. They planned to have only one sweeper on the whole compound, instead of having sweepers on every ward dealing with patients.

By mid-January 1922, he was overwhelmed with work:
"There is every possibility of the work proving too much. I may be compelled to neglect the medical work far more than is desirable. I must put all the facts before you. I feel now that I shall be free of all responsibility should I be unable to carry on."[43]

THE HOSPITAL IS COSTING THREE TIMES MORE

Money matters were pressing upon him: not only the financial problems of the hospital, but those arising from the fact that once again he was obliged to act as the local Mission Treasurer, with the responsibility for paying out all Mission grants, paying out all the salaries for teachers and evangelists and schools, arranging bills of exchange and coping with the financial problems of individual missionaries and their districts.[44]

Dr Roberts, was absolutely beaten by the need to provide complete annual accounts for the Mission, this was usually the whole time task of the Local Treasurer and he appealed for help. Happily he was relieved of the Local Treasurer's work by the arrival in Shillong of the Rev T. W . Reese from the Plains.

He was also greatly bothered by the fact that he could not find an assistant doctor to help him in a hospital that meant so much to him. Dr Roberts was facing the dilemma of having to pay more than a missionary's salary for a graduate Indian doctor, of any faith, to come and assist him. He was also finding that the grant made by the Mission to support the hospital was much too small and he was appealing for an increase of approximately £17 a month to raise the total grant to Rs 1000, or roughly £66 a month until they could earn more from their patients. Just for one minute imagine yourself running a hospital on £66 a month!

THE OPENING CEREMONY

At last the great day came when the hospital, with its true name displayed, was to be declared open by the Governor of Assam, in the presence of a large number of notables and the press, both local and national.[45] The programme which was handed to all the members of the audience made a declaration on its front page.

The Presbyterian Church of Wales
The Khasi Hills Welsh Mission Hospital
Jaiaw, Shillong, Assam

Medical Officer in Charge   Dr H. Gordon Roberts
Sister in Charge   Miss M. E. Buckley

The Opening Ceremony will take place on
Saturday the 25th March 1922 at 12 noon
His Excellency Sir William Marris, K.C.S.I., K.C.I.E.
Has kindly consented to perform the opening ceremony

An account of the opening ceremony was given in a letter by Mr H. J. Jones (brother of Mrs Katie Roberts), who was in India on a visit. He witnessed this most exciting event – the culmination of nearly ten years of dedication by his brother-in-law Dr Gordon Roberts from the beginning, and for the last two years with the added moral and spiritual strength of Miss Margaret Buckley. The building of the hospital started on 21 January 1915 and into it had been poured all of Dr Roberts' commitment together with the support he had received from the Presbyterian churches in Wales. H. J. Jones writes with flair:

"This is just a slight description of the Opening Ceremony, it would take a more facile pen than mine to do justice to it.

If you can imagine a large hill, from one side of which you can see a range of glorious hills to ascend which you must descend into a stretch of undulating land for at least ten miles, you will have some ideas of the beautiful spot on which the hospital is built.

The hospital itself had been the scene of strenuous activity for the preceding weeks, painting, polishing setting out, etc and the hundred and one details attended to that are so necessary for an occasion of this kind. The platform or dais had been erected at the side of the front porch because from that vantage point a larger space of ground was available. Both the dais and the drive leading to the porch were beautifully decorated with flowers and arches of green. At the entrance to the drive was a beautifully decorated arch with the words 'Khasi Hills Welsh Mission Hospital' on it, entwined with green foliage. It was decided that no distinction of class or rank should be recognised, with the single exception that the seats in the front row should be reserved for high Government officials. To look at the crowd from the vantage point of the dais was a most interesting scene. Hindus, Mahommedans, Khasis, Europeans and the Eurasians were mixed together in a heterogeneous mass. The multi-coloured dresses, together with the floral decorations, showed up against the more sombre background of the hospital itself.

Punctually at twelve noon, His Excellency arrived, attended by his staff. The staff by the way being in full dress uniform, and he was met at the entrance to the drive by Gordon and his staff (myself), but in our morning coats. At the foot of the dais were standing those who were to be presented to the Governor, viz the Rev Robert Jones, Rev Dr Edward Williams, the Rev Dr Oswald Williams, the Rev T W Reese and the Rai Sahib Dohory Ropmay.

His Excellency then passed up the steps to the dais itself and as soon as he seated himself, Mr Robert Jones gave out the opening hymn;

'Oh, Thou through suffering perfect made,
On whom the bitter Cross was laid,
In hour of sickness grief and pain
No sufferer turns to Thee in vain'.

It had been arranged to have a choir composed of Miss A.W. Thomas's girls and the Hostel boys. It was a truly representative choir composed of the various Hill tribes and they sang beautifully. They had been trained by Miss Thomas assisted by the Rev Sidney Evans.

Hardly had the passage of scripture been finished when Dr Edward Williams began his prayer. I cannot pretend to give you a resume of it, I can only tell you that it was referred to by the Governor in his speech, as a most eloquent one.

I should perhaps have mentioned that the passage of scripture read was the Parable of the Good Samaritan. It was read in Khasi by the Reverend Robert Jones.

Then came the great choral event of the ceremony, the singing of 'Now thank we all our God' by the choir. I do not, unfortunately, understand much about music, but they seemed to me to take the various parts splendidly and from the dais it sounded most pleasing. That it was so, was confirmed by the Governor himself, who made special reference to the singing to Gordon. At the last note Gordon was on his feet, looking probably more firm than he felt and delivering his carefully prepared oration.

I can only give you the *"oratia obliqua"*; time and space will not permit of the speech *"en gros"*. Beginning with a tribute to His Excellency, he passed on to an acknowledgement of the splendid work done by his medical missionary colleagues present, including a reference to Dr Fraser. He referred to the need for a hospital on the Khasi Hills and the loss that had been felt by the destruction of the Mission Hospital in Cherrapunji by the Great Earthquake of 1897. Passing on, he paid his tribute to the Government for having led the way throughout, and the splendid contribution to medical science by the Indian Medical Services. Finally he turned his attention to the present building, emphasising the need for it, the great financial outlay and the pressing need for future financial help and the consequent anxiety, winding up with a strong appeal for aid and closing with a statement of the motive that had inspired the undertaking.

He spoke with more than his usual clarity and was easily heard by all and I feel sure that he made a great impression on the audience generally. It was quite the piece de resistance of the whole show. He was I think, greatly appreciated by all classes of people.

Following on Gordon's speech the Ornamental Key was presented by the daughter of the Rai Sahib Ropmay (the Rai Sahib is practically the leading Khasi on the Hills). It had been arranged that Betty (Dr and Mrs Roberts' daughter) and the little Khasi girl should present it together, but poor Betty was in bed with a bad cold and had to be kept there and was not able to be present. It was a pity, as it would have added greatly to the effect to see both races represented in this little ceremony.

His Excellence then opened the door, which had been decorated with lilies, etc, and passed quickly into the hospital and as quickly round. He had already paid a preliminary visit of inspection some days before, so that his going in was more for forms sake than an actual visit. Returning to the dais he delivered his speech.

He paid a great tribute to Gordon, the hospital and all medical missionaries and as a mark of his appreciation of the work that Gordon had undertaken and brought to such a successful completion, he gave a contribution of Rs 5000 from a fund of Rs 15000 at his disposal. He concluded with quoting the words of Dr Williams' prayer.

Then followed a vote of thanks by the Reverend T. W. Reese who was in his happiest vein. He thanked His Excellency, referring to him as the hardest working man in the Province. He emphasised the loyalty of the Welsh nation and added that while the Khasis had no doubt caught many things from the Welsh missionaries, including the uncomfortable Welsh accent, they had also caught the Welsh spirit of loyalty.

He was followed very briefly by the Rai Sahib Ropmay, who seconded and confirmed what Rees had said.

Then came the Doxology, followed by *"God Save the King"* and ending with three cheers for the Governor, led by Reverend Robert Jones.

His Excellency was escorted by Gordon down to his car and drove off expressing his appreciation of the whole thing and his pleasure at being able to perform the opening ceremony. I should imagine that he really meant what he said.

The hospital was then thrown open to all and sundry. I should reckon that there were over 2000 present."[46]

POST SCRIPT TO THE OPENING CEREMONY

The event received national publicity in the dailies in Assam and great emphasis was placed upon the outstanding quality of the buildings, the completeness of the equipment and the fact that a nursing service was already being provided by Miss Buckley with pupil nurses.[47] The Governor's generosity was noted but more than all it was made clear that the whole project had been largely funded in the initial stages of building by Dr Gordon Roberts' own gifts, amounting to some thirty thousand rupees (£2,000), representing earnings while in the post of Civil Surgeon during the period of the War. This had inspired both the Government to make its grant of Rs sixty thousand (£4,000), and the people of Wales and Welsh Churches in England to contribute with unparalleled generosity to a fund which reached a total of about four hundred and fifty thousand rupees (£30,000).

The imagination of the Presbyterians in Wales and among the exiles in England (London, Manchester, Merseyside and the West Midlands in particular) had been fired and hearing about it had evoked a response from the people of the Khasi Hills and many individual donors from other communities in India. This gave the institution a certain distinction from the beginning. It evoked kindly feelings from very many good living people.

Apart from the manner in which the institution had been brought into being, immediate comparisons with other hospitals were made. It was said that it was an asset to the state; that there were few hospitals, even in the large cities of India, which could compare with the caring Christian love of the nursing staff and the dedication of Dr Roberts. For many years it was a measure by which other bigger hospitals were judged.

It was not long before other hospitals, sponsored mainly by the American Baptist Missions, were set up in Assam and a growing understanding between the staff of these hospitals was to prove vital in the later development of the nursing profession in Assam.

THE KHASI HILLS WELSH MISSION HOSPITAL BECOMES A WORKING INSTITUTION

It took eighteen months after the opening ceremony before the hospital really began to attract patients and the gradual growth in confidence shown by the Khasi community in the institution. Readiness to accept surgical solutions to their problems came slowly, but the care given by the nurses won the hearts of the inhabitants, and this of course resulted in the rapid increase in the number of girls applying for courses of training.

When the hospital scheme was being developed, the basis of the appeal set before the Government was that it would be for the Khasis only. It was not long before that was changed to all Indians, but resistance to the idea of admitting Europeans, planters and Government officials persisted for quite some time, until after the native patients began to be admitted. Then the inevitable happened and it was acknowledged that the hospital should be open for all who were in need of its services – even if they were European or Government servants! – but there was continued sniping at Dr Roberts for some years on the alleged grounds that he spent more time with the European patients than with the Indians.[48] It was nothing more than prejudice and a lack of good manners. He was furious at their lack of understanding: after all he was totally committed as a medical missionary who lived for his Saviour and for the people he had dedicated his life to bring them from 'darkness' into the 'light of the Gospel.' It seemed to have escaped the notice of these critics that among the European patients were missionaries of many missionary societies, who thanked God for the amenities of the Welsh Mission Hospital in the person of Dr Roberts, a kindly and proud Liverpool Welshman. They were surely colleagues to be helped, and deserved the same care and medical skill as the native Indians.

Indeed in his address to the British Medical Association, Dr Roberts stated clearly and without fear that *"in response to a demand from the European community, a European block has been erected and is at the present moment being extended."* It was a very brave move which astonished some of his preaching colleagues.

It was not the medical staff of the Mission who wanted to lay down such conditions but medically lay persons, backed by conservative opinions in the committees at home, who still persisted with the principle that medical missionary work was simply subservient to the work of evangelisation. For them in their committees in Falkner Street the medical missionary role was simply to render conversion more likely. The Khasi people, to whom the Gospel was extended by them, was the target population and therefore had a prior claim on the medical facilities. This prior claim was regarded by some of them almost as an exclusive right to admission, but later it was accepted that the patients from the field of labour of other missionaries, such as the Plains of Sylhet and Silchar, might be considered on that same basis, but still to be admitted within the walls of the hospital and they might yield converts if they came within the healing community of Shillong Welsh Mission Hospital. They were trying to conserve scarce resources for their main objective, the conversion of the Khasi Hills, but compassion cannot be circumscribed like that. It took time to learn the lesson.

Medical cases benefitted greatly from the special care given by the nurses. The mortality of the familiar cases like typhoid was greatly diminished, and the disciplined nursing was greatly valued.

It was not surprising therefore that before much time had elapsed, Dr Gordon Roberts was asked to give an account of his experience to the Annual General Meeting for 1926 of the Assam Branch of the British Medical Association, meeting in Silchar[49]

THE BRITISH MEDICAL ASSOCIATION IN SILCHAR

The British Medical Association in Assam was a very influential body much consulted by the Government and by the employing agencies, in particular the big tea companies in Calcutta. The members were almost exclusively British tea garden doctors with, of course, all the British medical servants of the Government itself, most of whom were in the Indian Medical Service.

Dr Gordon Roberts began with a resume of the medical background of the scheme which had been his passion, taking the opportunity of outlining the support which the Government had given them in the task of setting up a brand new hospital.

He mentioned the various Government officials who had helped him, the capital grant which had been given and the personal grant of Rs 5000 given by Sir William Marris, the Governor, when he opened the hospital.[50] Then he described the buildings, emphasising the hot water supply, the sanitary system, the wonders of the operating theatre with electrical sterilizers and the X-ray equipment, and the electrical apparatus for diathermy and high frequency treatment.

His remarks about nursing were among the most remarkable features of his account. *"The initial provision of one European sister being insufficient, a second sister was appointed and it is anticipated that the number will be increased to three at an early date. The hospital was opened with five Indian Christian nurses under training. The progress of the work has necessitated a marked increase in their number, which now stands at about forty. They are drawn from various parts of the Khasi Hills and at the present moment there are also three from Lushai."* It is worth noting that Dr Roberts mentioned that the supply of these nurses was greater than the demand. *"Girls of quite good families are becoming increasingly anxious to enter the nursing profession for they were aware of the atmosphere at the Hospital and the ethical standards demanded by Miss Buckley. All bedpan and other attendance is rendered by the nurses, and the sweeper – (we only need one for the whole hospital) – is not ordinarily required to enter the wards, which are cleaned by ward maids as at home."* Then he gave tribute to *"the nurses for their efficiency and reliability both in the wards and in the operating theatre."* He hoped that on the completion of their training they would be of considerable value to the districts from which they came.

This note of expectation was perhaps the first recognition in Assam that by the training of nurses, a new profession to serve the community was being created. Their acceptance of training gave grounds to hope that they would be of great help in the communities from which they came.

Dr Gordon Roberts went on to say that *"a maternity ward had recently been built with a labour ward capable of accommodating at least four patients at the same time if necessary."* A beginning had also been made with ante-natal work.

Admission Statistics	1923	1924	1925	Total
In-patients admitted	513	768	857	2,138
Indians	32	84	95	211
Europeans	545	852	952	2,349

Apart from the numerous minor operations the following major operations were performed:

	1923	1924	1925	Total
Total number Major Operations	176	198	280	654
Including Abdominal sections	63	90	102	235

In 1925, 66 appendectomies were performed, of this number:

    A. 17 were uncomplicated appendix disease

    B. 15 were removed during the operation of gastro-jejunostomy

    C. 34 were removed during various gynaecological operations.

Fully 90% of the appendices removed under the headings B and C were definitely diseased. His successor at the hospital, Dr R Arthur Hughes maintained that *"the operations proved beyond question that appendicitis is a very common trouble, at any rate in the Khasi Hills. It is however, much more common in its chronic form than in its acute form. Obviously one does not wish to be dogmatic as to its aetiology. One expects it most in cases of chronic constipation and it appears to vary readily following an attack of enteric fever or dysentery. One wonders how far a liberal diet of pork and dried fish can influence the situation. (A liberal diet of pork and dried fish would not be a very common privilege in those years amongst the Khasi people, and*

Dr. Hughes was able to tell me quite positively that Dr Roberts never once partook of either in all his years in Shillong!)"

There were a fair number of cases of acute appendicitis, chiefly among the tea planting community. Government officials seemed to be strangely immune. Without a doubt the emphasis on the finding of those in need among the planting community was, in part or largely due to the fact that the planter doctors would be strongly in favour of even a prophylactic appendectomy if there was any doubt or suspicion of pathology in that organ. An acute appendicitis in an isolated tea garden was potentially life threatening.

Dr Roberts reported a large number of cases of abdominal tuberculosis, *"and frequently, deposits round the ileo-caecal valve and in the neighbouring glands stimulate appendicitis with the recurrent fever and malaise stimulating malaria."*

Then Dr Roberts added:
"On first coming out to India we were told that almost all epigastric discomfort and pain was of hepatic origin – "it must be your liver" – but during the last five years we have been slowly proving that many of these cases of so-called "hepatic dyspepsia" are definite cases of gastric and duodenal ulcers, frequently accompanied by chronic appendicular disease."

Reporting this finding was surely something new to many of the planter doctors, to whom malaria, amoebic infections, dysentery and worms were the basic elements of all the pathology they knew. (Dr R Arthur Hughes met this same reaction after giving a paper to the British Medical Association in Shillong in 1940 on *"The Diagnosis of Acute Appendicitis"* when the comment was made that *"all these cases settled down with adequate treatment with emetine"* – the treatment then for amoebic dysentery).

Dr Roberts described enough surgical cases to make it quite evident that the former belief, propagated by many that did not have the existence of the Mission Hospital as one of their concerns, *"that there was very little surgery in the Hills"* was quite mistaken.

Dr Roberts went on to say: *"No reference has yet been made to gynaecology and obstetrics, which forms our chief work."* This is a revealing comment. Probably the Reverend Dr H G. Roberts was more at home in this aspect of medicine because his brief, and only post-graduate experience in Liverpool before he left for the Mission was in those specialities.

THE PROGRESS OF THE MATERNITY WORK AT THE NEW HOSPITAL

The number of delivery cases admitted	1923	1924	1925	Total
Normal	30	42	57	129
Abnormal	13	25	23	61
Total	43	67	80	190

Roughly half or the cases admitted in those three years were abnormal, but there were only two Caesarean sections performed at the hospital. There were number of cases of mothers who had presented late to the hospital with complications of labour. Some had uterine infections and sepsis as a result of an obstructed labour where the baby had died.These patients' babies had to have a craniotomy and their mothers underwent Caesarean section in an attempt to remove the source of the sepsis and to save the mothers' lives. Dr Roberts pinned his hope for improvement on persuading cases to arrive for ante-natal supervision. This field was an important part of the training of nurses in preparation for their role in the villages after completing their courses. Vesico-vaginal fistulae (an abnormal connection between the bladder and the vagina) after difficult labour were far too common and the variety generally seen was that associated with destruction of the internal sphincter. Operative attempts to heal were extremely disappointing to a keen observer like Dr Roberts.

The consecrated surgeon ended his talk with the statement that *"the upkeep of the hospital required over Rupees 50,000 per annum. The Mission was only able to contribute about Rupees 8,000 of this amount and so the income had very largely to be raised from the fees of private patients. Many gifts were received from grateful patients."* Giving this warning, the dedicated doctor was able to tell the Mission Board in Liverpool at the end of 1926 that he would not ask for further regular maintenance grants for the hospital.

The address created great interest. The statistics which were given surprised most of those present. For the first time they could add to their resources in Assam a hospital which provided modern amenities, and, in Dr Gordon Roberts, one who was prepared to tackle surgical problems and who could bring investigative methods within reach of those who lived in Assam. They could see him as an iconoclast of some of their old clinical mythologies who was able to venture into the world of medicine to bring surgical techniques into play to effect cures.

The doctors learnt with surprise that in Shillong they could not only train, but that they could also select, from a number of candidates, in particular girls for training as nurses. The girls who offered themselves as candidates were all from first or second generation Christian families. This was a factor in the success of the training, for their faith helped them to overcome the hurdles of traditional practices and prejudices and enabled them to establish the beginning of a new ethic of care.

THE BRITISH MEDICAL ASSOCIATION SEES FOR ITSELF THE NEW HOSPITAL

A year later the British Medical Association held its annual general meeting in Shillong itself and delegates were invited to visit the hospital and to see for themselves the 'wondrous miracles that had been achieved.' They had never seen the like of it in Assam. At the end of the tour the President made the following remarks:

*"One more point gentlemen. Last year at the meeting in Silchar
we had the great privilege of listening to a paper by Dr H. Gordon
Roberts on one aspect of his work in the Welsh Mission Hospital. We
feel, and I think that you will agree, that no more remarkable hope had
ever been read to us, a veritable landmark in medical work in Assam.
Personally, to me, it was a revelation and I came away profoundly
impressed. Unquestionably this hospital has assumed the character of
a national asset, standing behind us as it does, in times of stress and
difficulty and placing into the hands of each one of us the possibility of
a clean curative and comprehensive surgery for our patients, even in
cases most acute, and to the expectant mother a welcome relief from
the heat of the Plains. Cannot we as a body show our gratitude to this
institution in a practical way? The Province as such does nothing at
all at present. We confidently leave the fulfilment of this duty to your
mature consideration. The time is opportune and public opinion is
crystallized. We should lead the way."* [51]

The form of the support which the members of the British Medical
Association gave to the hospital was to send a regular stream
of patients there through the years. In spite of the fact that other
Mission Hospitals were developed later, and they were much nearer
the tea gardens, patients continued to come to Shillong. This was
partly because the climatic conditions there surpassed anything that
could be found on the Plains during the rains or the hot weather and
also because a number of the doctors had developed a degree of
professional loyalty and real affection for the place and the staff.

A time came when the development of air travel in the Assam Valley with India and the international air lines, made it easier for patients from some tea areas to fly directly to Calcutta in less time than it took to come up to Shillong by road. Indeed it became possible for complex cases to reach London in very little more time than used to be necessary to reach Shillong, but this was only to happen after the Second World War and the Declaration of India's Independence. Of much greater significance was the increasing capacity of the other Mission Hospitals belonging to the American Baptist Missions at Jorhat, Tezpur and Gauhati which were much nearer to the people to cope with the problems, and finally came the development of the Medical College Hospitals at Dibrugarh and Gauhati at various times after Independence in 1947.

THE SIMON COMMISSION VISITS SHILLONG

In January 1929 Shillong was visited by the Simon Commission, the most notable of the visiting commissions to tour India. Its brief was to gather information concerning the possibility of responsible political developments in India. Lady Simon visited the hospital, indeed it seemed to be almost obligatory for notables visiting Shillong to visit the hospital. Despite the opposition of the major political parties to the constitution and mandate of the Commission leading to their boycott of its meetings in many parts of India, there were a number of Shillong ladies who met them, including some of the Khasi ladies, who were by this time becoming influential in the social field and in education.

THE HOSPITAL FINDS GOOD FRIENDS IN THE SHILLONG COMMUNITY

When the Government gave the grant of Rs 60,000 to the hospital funds in 1919 a condition was slipped into the terms of the grant, that the hospital would provide the X-ray facilities and perform all the X-ray work and electro-therapeutic work necessary for Government servants without payment and in perpetuity. This condition was inoperative for some years and perhaps Dr Roberts did not find that the condition created any great drain during the early years. Three years had passed after the grant was made before the hospital was opened and there was a further lapse of time before the electrical power system was fully functioning and the X-ray equipment could be operated. By this time, 1925, they did have an X-ray set with an eleven inch spark gap which could take a chest X-ray in about a minute, but like all machines of its type, it was a little temperamental. It could give dramatic displays of a corona of light around the overhead cables and startling showers of sparks around the X-ray tube. It would indeed be surprising to get very satisfactory results with it but in some cases the psychological effects on villagers were remarkable.

In May 1925 a letter came from Colonel Innes, the Inspector General of Civil Hospitals and Prisons, asking whether the X-ray apparatus was functioning.

Dr Roberts wrote to Colonel Innes "asking for the cancellation of the agreement re: X-ray service". A fairly prompt answer suggested that the condition might be waived and that a regular arrangement for the provision of services on payment be established. This system Dr Roberts accepted and later the Mission confirmed the new arrangement. The Viceroy and Sir John Kerr visited in 1926.51

In January 1932 Sir Laurie and Lady Hammond promoted a Great Fete on the games field below the Mission Boys' Hostel to further an appeal for a new X-ray set.52 The Hammonds were personally involved and gave great assistance. The Governor's Private Secretary acted as Master of Ceremonies, the Regimental Band played and tents were provided for the various sideshows. The fete attracted *"everybody"* in Shillong: there were about four thousand attendees. The proceeds amounted to six thousand rupees, enough to buy the X-ray table and some additional electro-medical equipment.

An event like this would of course be publicised in all the papers and would bring to the notice of patients and doctors that within a short time the hospital would be well equipped with an up-to-date X-ray machine. It was indeed a vast improvement on the old machine but was still limited because it was ultimately dependent upon the electricity generating system in the hospital and its large storage battery. This provided direct current of course. This necessitated the use of a rotary convertor, which only gave power enough to operate the X-ray apparatus at one third its designated power. Despite this limitation it still gave quite good service and the more modern controls and fittings considerably enhanced the ability of the set to give satisfactory images.

Finding staff to operate the machine presented problems for a decade or more.

THE MAHARANI OF GWALIOR COMES TO THE HOSPITAL FOR SURGERY

Miss Amy Bullock, who nursed the Maharani in May 1931 wrote:

"The senior Maharani of Gwalior arrived in Shillong seeking cure from a serious illness. She was accompanied by ladies in waiting and counsellors and doctors and an astrologer. She belonged to a very orthodox Hindu caste and had been to several States and seen various doctors and surgeons, but could not make up her mind to be treated by any of them. The fame of the Welsh Mission Hospital had spread and the news that there were good Khasi nurses to care for patients had reached her, so she arrived in Shillong with all her entourage and took a whole boarding house for the summer.

Her senior physician, together with other senior Government doctors came to the hospital to consult Dr Roberts. They decided that he should be allowed to see the Maharani and to examine her, but only a very small portion of her anatomy being exposed, a very difficult way to make a diagnosis! She consented to have the operation performed under certain conditions which necessitated a good part of the private wards being set apart for her use, together with accommodation for the 'Ajibhai Saheb' (a grandmother) and the physician, the ladies in waiting and the Minister of State. The latter came during the day and sat in a large room in the lower block.

Added to this, the astrologer used the summer house on the lawn to predict when things were to take place. Dr Gordon Roberts informed the physician that the prediction regarding the time for the operation would have to be at a time convenient to him and it was agreed to do it at nine in the morning. (A hen had been killed and hung up in the Maharani's room). All went well and the Maharani was very pleased with the way the Khasi nurses attended her.

A gift of thirty-two thousand rupees expressed the Maharani's appreciation of the kindness shown to her. Dr Roberts of course refused to take as a personal gift the eighteen thousand rupees which was delivered as a gift for Mrs Roberts and the two children, David and Betty. A further fourteen thousand rupees was sent for the matron and the nursing staff. These two sums together were a very substantial help towards defraying the cost of massive building repairs to counter the activities of white ants in the timber work of the main block." [52]

The coming of such an important personage to have surgical treatment, and her praise of the Khasi nurses, brought the hospital, and Dr Roberts' name, still more under the spotlight of public acclaim, particularly since the Maharani was a much travelled person who spoke several European languages. She had seen the world and yet she chose to come to Shillong and the Welsh Mission Hospital. This was a very considerable accolade.[53]

She wrote again to Dr Roberts after leaving Shillong detailing her thanks to all the staff, but alas she died a few months later of a condition for which there was then no treatment.

There were more distinguished visitors to the hospital in 1932. Dr Henry Houghton, one of the two medical commissioners of the (American) Laymen's Foreign Missionary Enquiry paid a visit.[54] His visit was symptomatic of a great change coming over many missionary societies which had hitherto withheld support from medical missionary work in hospitals, although they may have sanctioned some dispensary activities. Even these dispensaries were sometimes conducted strictly as spare time activities to be supported by patients' fees but with no right to any support from mission grants. Dr Houghton in a letter to Dr Gordon Roberts after his visit stated *"how profitable it was for me to visit your unrivalled institution. There is not one hospital in any missionary field which I have visited which comes nearer to the ideal of giving the best that Christians of the West possess to the needy people of the East, nor yet one which expresses more correctly the spirit of the Gospel as it is made manifest through the ministry of healing the sick. It is a place which gives a man inspiration. We came away with a new vision of the un-ending power which is in the Christian advance."* Dr Houghton's visit was with the intention of assessing the role of medical missionary work in the overall pattern of evangelistic missions.

In the decade 1925-35 a number of missionary hospitals were opened in Assam, mainly by American Baptist churches, the first being a hospital for women in Gauhati on the initiative of the Women's Council of the Assam Baptist Convention.

A second visitor was General Sir John Shea, G O C Eastern Command who inspected the hospital and its resources and approved the recognition of the hospital for the treatment of military cases, setting specific fees for the treatment given.[55] This recognition was still valid when the hospital became involved in the treatment of cases coming from the Burma front in 1941-3, and it probably pre-empted the step of taking over the hospital for the use of the military.

PERSONALITIES AND MISS MARGARET BUCKLEY

There is no doubt that Miss Margaret Buckley was an outstanding nurse. The testimony from one of her very first nurses recognised that she was strong mentally and physically and was quite prepared to drive others as hard as she drove herself. She did not have much time to spare for weaklings unless they were patients, in which case she threw all her energies into making them better and did her best to inculcate them with some of her own spirit and give them of her own strength.[56]

Two missionary sisters came out to help in the hospital whose background included the same kind of training as Miss Buckley herself had received. Neither of these had the physical energy of Miss Buckley nor her strength of will.

In January 1929 Miss Amy Katherine Bullock, with a totally different type of training came out and she began, with the help of Dr Drinsingh Hynniewta, to make the lectures she had received during the course of her training in King's College Hospital, London, accessible to the student nurses in the Welsh Mission Hospital.[57] Dr Drinsingh was a master of the Khasi language and he translated and converted the idioms of Kings College into Khasi. All the teaching of nurses at the hospital at this stage was given in Khasi and Miss Bullock had to learn the language with precision in order to lecture and explain, both in the classroom and on the wards.

It was completely evident from the beginning of this teaching that it was at a level, or on a pattern, radically different from the teaching given by Miss Buckley, and that she, and the other two sisters had been given in their training. Their practical skills were exemplary at the therapeutic level asked of them at that time, and their dedication to the evangelistic challenge was beyond reproach. The aim of the new approach to training was to give nurses a greater understanding of the nature of diseases and the reason why specific treatments were given. They were no longer to be the exponents of *"Practical Nursing"* in the tradition of Florence Nightingale and the District Nurses, but rather to belong to that school of nurses who could understand doctors talking about pathology and anatomy and the new understanding of disease processes, and to be as skilful in the care and comforting of patients as any *"Practical Nurse"*. Increasingly they were also expected to become proficient in the use of technical procedures which had not been imagined before. With confidence one can say that none of the old school of nurses, those of the first fifteen years, had ever (for example) seen a blood transfusion given.

The new training and practice represented the difference between accepting that the cause of pneumonia was not a chill but the pneumococcus - the micro-organism of lobar pneumonia, or in other words that it was an infection.

THE ART OF NURSING WAS BEING TRANSFORMED IN SHILLONG BY PROGRESS IN MEDICAL SCIENCE

Once again the emphasis is clear that there is no end to change in medicine, the graph of progress never comes to a final plateau but goes on inexorably upwards. In the course of that movement, it is inevitable that the special skills of individuals are superseded and their understanding surpassed. Even those who pioneer advances will always find that their juniors, whom they taught, will excel them in due course in skill and understanding and knowledge. It needs grace and joyful commitment to the chief end of the discipline to be able, at all times, to accept relegation. This is no easier in the missionary context.

It is entirely understandable that one who had pioneered nursing in Shillong and who had deserved and received much praise, and the Kaiser-i-Hind Silver Medal for the services she had rendered, would feel estranged by the changes taking place, however tactfully they might be introduced.[58] It was not nursing colleagues and equals that Miss M Buckley wanted to carry out the work, but nurses who would do what they were told. Dr Roberts once told Dr R Arthur Hughes that she had the sense, denied to many others, which enabled her, when she had been out of the hospital for a few hours, to know precisely just what the nurses had been doing. She also had the ability to be able to predict what Dr Roberts himself would be doing next. She was not easily persuaded to follow paths of what seemed to be wisdom to ordinary people. When she was advised, recommended, urged to go to bed because she was ill, or to take a holiday so that she might rest, she rarely agreed. Indeed at one stage Dr Roberts pleaded with the General Secretary in Liverpool to instruct her to take a holiday. It could very fairly be said of her that she carried into hospital the philosophy of a competent District Nurse in the Welsh Valleys at the turn of the century, who knew in their heart of hearts that it was nursing which brought the patient through the illness and that doctors were incidental, required to prescribe, or even to operate, or to give a name to the condition which was to be treated, but the nurses healed them - of course with God's will. In many situations at the end of the previous century that faith would not have been far wrong and it would have been especially true with the poor who could not afford to have a visiting doctor.

Miss Buckley was an autonomous authority, devoted to the care of her patients, dedicated to the missionary cause, and she knew best. Such characteristics are those of the pioneers She took up a new challenge and moved from Shillong in 1934 to take charge of the hospital in Jowai, left without a missionary in charge since the death of Dr Edward Williams.

Her departure to Jowai was not uneventful, and neither did it take place without much heart burning and criticism of Dr Gordon Roberts by some of the missionary colleagues who belonged to that same generation which valued the *"Practical Nurse"* and themselves practised the arts of the *"Doctor in the Home"*, who prescribed medicine and ran dispensaries without any medical experience.

In Jowai however she started again in the same manner as in the beginning in Shillong.[59] She did not want a missionary nursing colleague but would rather have half a dozen good Khasi nurses with the stamp of her training upon them. They would do what they were told; a missionary colleague might have different opinions.[60]

Nursing training in Shillong developed on a pattern which corresponded with that given to nurses in the United Kingdom. The initial educational requirements asked of the candidates for entry into the training school in Shillong gradually rose but there were few who had achieved matriculation before entry until after the State Registration Act was passed.

THE RECRUITMENT OF DOCTORS

It was not surprising that the recruitment of national doctors should follow the pattern in Government service. There were very few graduate doctors in the land and they either opted into Government service and enjoyed the emoluments of those appointments, or, if they entered other employment or private practice they expected that the financial rewards would be commensurate. These rewards exceeded the levels that missionary societies were prepared to pay their medical missionaries. Licentiate doctors, men and women who had followed shorter courses of training in less prestigious schools with less well qualified teachers, were beginning to appear. Young people from the Hill tribes were being given stipends by the Government to enable them to qualify in such schools. From among this group of doctors a number gave loyal and effective service to the Welsh Presbyterian Mission in its various hospitals through the years.

Recruiting missionary colleagues with graduate qualifications proved to be an even more difficult problem all through the years to the very end of the story. One problem was that doctors with a missionary vocation were very thin on the ground at any time and many of those who ventured to express an interest had their own reservations about what they would like to do. One point of view stated that to go out to build a hospital and spend some years perhaps doing something for which they were not trained was not their idea of using their God-given gifts and training. Dr Roberts had of course done that, he had a call to build a hospital and he did it, triumphantly. Having had the call and responded remarkably, he felt disturbed if a potential candidate indicated that they would be prepared in principle to take over the surgery. Only one or two actually possessed postgraduate experience and qualifications to justify such a suggestion and displace Dr Roberts with his increasing experience. Dr Roberts wondered if there would be work enough for the men with similar surgical interests. Then he would point out that there would surely be tremendous scope for such work in the Lushai Hills or in the Plains of Sylhet. (He even gave a large sum of money from the income of the Welsh Mission Hospital in Shillong to a fund so they could build a hospital in Durtlang in the Lushai Hills). At various times he expressed the thought that so great was the need that, ideally, four or five hospitals should be built, and then he would come back to the thought that to have two doctors in Shillong working together in all amity would cover many emergencies, solve furlough problems, enable extensions of the work, perhaps to villages and other dispensaries and prevent the collapse of the work which might result if the one man fell ill or went home. It was quite evident that if a second man were to come to Shillong that he would be the one to whom fell the privilege of starting these new developments.

He discussed these points in his correspondence with the General Secretary in Liverpool. He questioned whether his desire to have another colleague in Shillong was possibly selfish when his missionary colleagues in the Plains or Cachar or Lushai pleaded for a doctor.

The net result of this complex was that Dr Gordon Roberts never did have a missionary colleague to work with him until the very end of his own career in Shillong, when Dr R Arthur Hughes came out in 1939.[61] Only during his periods of home leave was there another British doctor working in the hospital. In the earlier years the Civil Surgeon of Shillong acted in his place but in later years the amount of work involved was far too great to permit it to be done on a part-time basis.

Not to have a professional colleague of equal or greater competence in any or all aspects of the clinical work was a tremendous deprivation, especially when there were advances in medical science which would be entirely relevant in the local situation.

THE LAST FIVE YEARS BEFORE
THE SECOND WORLD WAR

During the last five years, before the war in Burma came close to Assam to touch the life of the whole country, Dr Roberts seemed to be concerned to do all that he could to complete the hospital and its equipment.

One aspect of this intention was to confirm the policy of self-sufficiency as far as possible. Even though communications had improved a great deal, Calcutta was still as far away as ever, and now there were still more institutions and organisations calling for the services of experts from agency houses in Calcutta. One aspect of the concern for practical self-sufficiency was to yield to the pressure of opinion from his own staff to equip the engine room with a variety of machine tools which would enable them to effect repairs and make new equipment. It seems that the initiative for the purchase of this engine room equipment came from Bah Elwin. Dr Gordon Roberts had immense confidence in him and dependence upon his knowledge and judgement in the mechanical and electrical field. He was very fortunate in Bah Elwin in the engine room as well as Bah

Drickson, his building collaborator. Dr Roberts put his trust in these two men and it was this which enabled him to do so much when he himself was only capable, as it were, of making the policy decision. Dr Roberts would mention some piece of equipment he would like to have and talk about it in the hearing of Bah Elwin, who would then immediately convert it into a practical proposition with a precision which was quite remarkable considering that he only used a steel rule and a calliper. Besides the mechanical engineering and the making of new equipment, which might require welding, or brazing, or casting and machining brass or lead or aluminium, the men in the engine room were competent in all the routine electrical work, re-wiring and fixing switches and fuses or burnt-out elements, even rewinding commutators for the many electrical motors driving theatre pumps and suction apparatus and fans. Even delving inside the older diathermy machines and X-ray apparatus with an electric bell and a Leclanche battery was not beyond their field of interest.

They did all the plumbing and sanitary work for the hospital, they did all the steam pipe work and all the alterations to the boiler; they repaired and replaced steam valves and could even make simple valves for ward apparatus such as sterilisers and water heaters. There were no trade union problems, or demarcation disputes, no caste problems either, but there was among them a recognition that one particular man handled brazing copper pans best, and this other man matters electrical on the domestic scale, and so on. It was the chief cook from the steam kitchen who was deputed to wind all the ward clocks every week; he held a solemn round with a bunch of keys and a large alarm clock with "standard hospital time" and he corrected and wound each clock, but Elwin could teach them all. He was the one who would reply to Dr Roberts' query as to the possibility of doing a certain thing with the words "Why not?"[62]

THE SELF-SUFFICIENT POLICY OF DR GORDON ROBERTS

Dr Roberts, the founder of the hospital, had established as a founding principle the need to be self-sufficient in all things which, if they went wrong, might require the assistance of a maintenance engineer from Calcutta, at huge expense. Providentially he had gathered together a group of men headed by Elwinton Gatphoh who gained the ability to do wondrous works with piping, whether it carried steam or water; with electric cables and switchgear; blown fuses and burnt-out kettles, or commutators on electric motors; caring for diesel engines or a Morcom High Speed single cylinder steam engine driving the electricity generator was also within their remit. They could manage a large lead battery which stored electricity for the night. They could explore the inside of an X-ray machine using a Leclanche cell and an electric bell to determine the health of circuits. They cast metals, they turned brass or steel, they fabricated equipment. Elwin's motto was always "Why not – we'll try". Nothing pleased them more than a challenge to do new things instead of being asked to do the boring maintenance jobs which the nurses asked them to do, replacing fuses or fitting lightbulbs and the like. The chaotic condition of Calcutta gave every incentive to continue the DIY tradition because the demands for equipment and engineers created a highly competitive and expensive situation.

It so happened that problems relating to steam were the most clamant. The production of steam from the big boiler using the dirtiest coal that could be imagined, for it contained 18% ash brought in pony carts from Cherrapunji thirty miles away,raised its own problems.

A chance viewing of a book entitled The efficient Use of Steam which was evidently a wartime economy campaign production, brought light to the situation. Written by a chief engineer of the Tate and Lyle sugar factory in Liverpool and enlightened with skilfully chosen quotations from Alice in Wonderland or parodies of Tennyson's Hiawatha and many other sources, it reduced some of the principles of the use of steam to simple rules which the layman could understand. So began the campaign for economy in the hospital.

First of all they insulated the boiler and the piping. Then they directed the exhaust steam from the steam engine through pipes in the bottom of a large tank, providing the hot water required for the wards. They acquired some superannuated hot water radiators from an army dump in Calcutta and broke each one up into three sections, then used them to replace the infinitely dirty coal fires in the wards (fires which seemed to have a greater output of soot than of heat) by connecting up those radiators to a steam supply pipe. The condensed water from the radiators was piped back to the boiler house to provide pre-heated water for the boiler itself. All of this brought about great economies in the use of coal and for the first time secured cleanliness by the elimination of soot from the wards and made possible the appearance of really white bed linen and uniforms. With balanced pressure steam traps they modernised the sterilising apparatus and the steam kitchen for the general wards .Subsequently they had to buy a new and bigger steam boiler to cope with increasing needs as the hospital grew.

They wasted nothing in the hospital: toothpaste tubes in those early days were still made of tin, and all the toothpaste tubes from the wards and the nurses hostel were collected and melted down to make solder. The aluminium tops of penicillin bottles were collected and melted down and so on. They made beds for the wards and theatre were made with galvanised piping to their own design, much more robust and cheaper than factory made beds from Calcutta.

As the anaesthetic techniques and operative surgical work became more complex they needed oxygen and they began to make their own oxygen. The point of this was that when the hospital needed oxygen they had to send the empty cylinders to Calcutta and then wait up to three months for them to be returned to Shillong after filling. The cost of sending the heavy iron cylinders to Calcutta and the delays were a constant annoyance and uncertainty, so it was decided that they should make their own. They obtained an electrolytic cell through which a low-voltage current was passed and the oxygen released from the water in the cell was collected in a gasometer and piped to the theatre and maternity ward. It served for a number of years very well.

Wherever patients with emphysema, for example, required constant oxygen, small domestic-sized oxygen concentrators were used. When oxygen was supplied in cylinders which had to be carried a long distance, these oxygen concentrators were a great blessing. The fresh air from which the oxygen was filtered off was plentiful. This was progress par excellance as a talented Physician reminded me when he read this section. The operating theatres provided plenty of scope for home manufacture of equipment. They made shadowless lamps of considerable efficiency, and anaesthetic tables, and adapted the EMO to new techniques. Then in the war years there were suction apparatuses made from army scrap and constant drainage systems from aquarium aerators put into reverse. They proved effective and they were fun to make according to Dr R A Hughes; the whole process of working out the details stimulated them to learn a great deal more about the problem. All of this work proved cheaper than a perfect model bought from the specialists, and when it went wrong, they knew how it could be repaired.

In the laboratory at the hospital they made a semi-automatic burette for titrations when carrying out a test much used in those days, the Fractional Test Meal. This saved much time and gave a gain in accuracy.

Producing boiling water for tea in the wards had been effected by the use of massive black kettles suspended over coal fires in each ward kitchen, a dirty and even dangerous practice.

All these innovations kept the Khasi engineers at the hospital content and convinced them that they were making a valuable contribution to the superhuman efforts of the Dr Roberts and his nursing staff. They had been instrumental in saving a great deal of money, solving the soot problem which had been so devastating and therefore facilitating cleanliness.

Any person from outside the hospital who came to visit Dr Roberts would always be shown around the engine room. It brought confidence to the remarkable self-taught native engineers.

When Dr Wilder, at that time Secretary of the Christian Medical Association of India, toured Assam's mission hospitals he was greatly impressed by the engineering team. All the staff contributed to the success of the hospital. The laundry men, the cook, all were involved in the welfare of the patients, and they also attended the cottage meetings or the monthly service in the Hall of the hospital. The carpenters were at hand to prepare walking aids of light wood as well as proving their expertise with splints.

When he was in Wales on leave, Dr Roberts would consult good friends about his problems. Many of these advisers were friends recruited by his old minister the Revd J. D. Evans who had moved to minister at St David's Presbyterian Church of Wales chapel in Pontypridd. Mr Arthur Lloyd Thomas of Pontypridd was one of these friends and he was a most notable adviser. He had been Commissioner for Housing during the First World War and he knew a great number of people in South Wales. It was he who selected the new steam-powered generator producing 30KVA at 110 volts DC. He selected the laundry equipment and other strategic items through firms in South Wales. Dr H. G. Roberts therefore had technical help in Wales and he believed that if the equipment selected was delivered in Shillong with the appropriate construction book, that Bah Elwin would be able to put it together and set it up. Whenever something big had been set up like the steam engine, Dr Roberts would be there to inspire and back them, making suitable grunting noises at appropriate moments and entering into the excitement of effort, but never being rash enough to give specific instructions. Dr Roberts had no fear whatever about this and the fruit of such confidence is seen in parts of his Final Report.

THE FINAL REPORT

In a letter to the directors in Liverpool, dated 10 August 1942, Dr Roberts gave a final report.[63] By this time he had already retired from the hospital and did no clinical or administrative work. But he had an outstanding nursing staff. In 1937 he had the service and dedication of Menna Jones from Ysbyty Ifan, Wales.[64]

This nine page letter acknowledges a letter from the General Secretary in Liverpool Reverend Oliver Thomas (1887-1950) dated 20 February 1942 in which he was asked for a summary of past financial and capital transactions and for an account of what he had invested in buildings and equipment during his period in office. (There was in this letter a specific attempt to ascertain what Dr Roberts would be passing over to his successor in the hospital and how it had come to pass). This letter provides a useful framework on which to set out an account of the last years of Dr Roberts' stewardship.

First came a list of financial statements covering quarterly statements of upkeep, income and expenditure for 1941 and 1942 and comparative statements for 1939, 1940 and 1941. These covered the period of the initial involvement of the hospital in all the events in Shillong arising because of the War. Then came a summary of the capital expenditure, together with a list of all the equipment sent through the Mission Head Office between 1937 and 1942, and finally, a total summary account, showing the capital expenditure on the hospital from 1913 to June 30 1942. It was a typical Dr Roberts review. He appended to this some brief comments in reply to questions which had been asked by the Committee.

(a) The total capital expenditure on the hospital from the beginning up to June 30, 1942 was £66542/12/3.

(b) The total sum spent on the hospital buildings since the hospital was first started was £34126/10/8. These new buildings include the original (1922) complement shown on the hospital plan and those added mainly in the 1930s viz:

1. The New Private Patients Ward Block
2. A New Operating Theatre
3. The Boiler House

4. Building for the New Steam Laundry Plant
5. New Servants Quarters

He writes in greater detail:

1.   These buildings include the Private Wards block No. 2 which
    was built entirely out of savings on Private Patients' fees. The
    block is a very substantial building on modern lines, partly
    constructed of concrete. Tiling has been extensively used and
    all the rooms are regarded as up-to-date. (The late Governor,
    who was a patient, expressed himself as extremely pleased with
    everything).

*"A further extension of great value to the business side of the
hospital has been a new office. This was specially necessary because
of the increased amount of clerical work now done which necessitates
the employment of two full-time clerks." (Dr Roberts had always done
the keeping of accounts, the safe for the hospital was in his study in
the bungalow, and he would spend three or four hours a day on the
business of the hospital and on supervising the progress of building
projects). All this provided a difficult set of duties to be undertaken
by his successor, Dr Hughes, who was totally ignorant of business
procedures but who was nevertheless obliged to undertake this work.
In some measure there was a reversal of the priorities which had
governed Dr Roberts' last years in the hospital. During this time Dr
Roberts had done little or no clinical work and had spent most of his*

time on administration. For Dr Hughes the work with the patients came first and all the time. The business was a matter of home work into the small hours of the night. It was several years later before he was able to take advantage of the opportunity to re-employ retired Government servants (at 55 years of age), to undertake more and more of the routine office work."

Dr Gordon Roberts continues:

"The goods which had been despatched in 1937 and 1938 had to be suitably housed and this involved the erection of:

(1) A large boiler house in close proximity to the engine room. It was only possible by an extensive excavation into the slope of the hill above. The boiler concerned was some fifteen feet tall and about five feet in diameter. (The re-siting of this boiler from the place where it was originally set involved felling the boiler onto its side to lie on a sled of telegraph poles padded with sacksful of ashes and dragging this up on rollers, by man power and the aid of a windlass, some fifty yards on the flat, then changing its course and pulling it up a steep slope to a point above the pit which had been dug, changing the direction again, and letting it down some twenty-five feet to stand on the floor of the pit below and, finally, moving it in the erect position to its final seating."

This was one of the first feats of co-operative effort which Dr Hughes and his wife, Mrs Nancy Hughes, saw when they arrived in Shillong in 1939 and it filled them with a sense of awe at the readiness of Elwin and his crew to tackle huge physical tasks. It was only later that they appreciated that the Khasis had in times long past erected great standing monoliths to celebrate great occasions. These were monoliths which they had dragged for miles, as happened with the stones of Stonehenge, if they were brought all the way from Pembrokeshire.

In order to comply with municipal requirements a very tall reinforced concrete chimney had to be erected. (This became one of the most noteworthy landmarks for travellers up the road from Gauhati to Shillong, for this stood out above everything else as the town of Shillong came to view).

"(2) The new steam laundry had been housed in a suitable building to the plans given by Arthur Lloyd Thomas.

(3) Three blocks of servants' quarters had been built to a much better hygienic standard than the previously existing accommodation. These housed the engine-room men, the boiler men, the laundry men, the cooks, the messengers and more. (It was in these small houses, in terraces, that the weekly cottage meetings took place when the hospital had acquired a pastor).

(4) Four thousand feet of two-inch piping had been laid to bring water downhill from a great municipal tank a mile away in Mawkhar to the hospital. For many years the municipality provided 20,000 gallons of water daily, freely to the hospital.

(5) A new electrical wiring system had to be installed on the behest of the Government inspector. All conductors had to run underground."

Dr Roberts then wrote of the advantages to the hospital secured by these new buildings and equipment.

THE BOILER

This was purchased at the cost of £531, after consultation with
Arthur Lloyd Thomas (and Dr Roberts describes the technical details
in his own style):

*"who had arranged with the makers that it should supply sufficient
steam to provide:*

1. *Heat for the boiling of all the bath water required for the
   hospital. (Dr Gordon Roberts was always keen on the availability
   of hot baths.)*
2. *Adequate steam for the maintenance of a large hospital steam
   kitchen.*
3. *Sufficient steam to supply the needs of the various steam
   sterilisers in different parts of the hospital; for maintaining food
   warming cupboards and bedpan sterilisers.*
4. *Sufficient steam under pressure to operate a large new electrical
   engine able to supply current for our whole outlay.*
5. *Steam to operate our new steam laundry plant."*

These five requirements lead themselves to further discussion
for they once represented an advanced view of the needs of the
hospital, but changes in medical practice and a changing population
quite quickly made some of the forward looking arrangements into
anachronisms. They just didn't fit any longer. Reviewing these points
again, we are told:

1. Enough hot water for baths for the doctors and nurses. The provision seemed well designed until the number of nurses and doctors increased and then the adequacy of the water supply became the critical factor. For patients in the private wards, changes in practice were influential in making the provision of baths seem inadequate. In the days when patients were kept strictly in bed for ten days after an appendectomy and for a fortnight after childbirth, the number of patients mobile enough to take advantage of bathroom provisions was small, but later, when major abdominal surgical cases were expected to walk on the day after operation, then queues for the use of bathroom facilities developed. Baths were an integral part of Dr Gordon Roberts' view of life in hospital, or in any domestic situation in India, and he provided extravagantly according to the opinion of the time.

2. The Steam Kitchen in which was cooked all the food for the general ward patients and the nurses, was a product of the hospital workshop. Elwin's reading, as he sat for his shift by the side of the steam engine at the end of a day's work, usually consisted of a browse through one of the large catalogues published by some of the great agency houses in Calcutta, especially Jessops. A picture of such a steam kitchen would have featured in these pages and on the basis of the picture and the brief description Elwin planned for its construction and Dr Roberts was very ready to procure the materials to implement the idea. This kitchen was the pride and joy of the cooks who worked in it. The walls were tiled with white tiles throughout, and a fly could

be easily spotted. The whole unit formed a boxed in table some eight circular openings cut in the thick shining steel plate forming the top of the unit accommodated the copper and brass pans in which the cooking took place. The pans fitted into steam jackets and were heated directly. The steam supply was regulated by shining steel wheel valves which protruded from the side face of the table. There was no smoke and no dirt. Each and every day the large pans were filled with rice, or dhal, or curry, or vegetables, or eggs, sometimes with chicken. Sometimes they fried dried fish to go with the rice and dhal, but when there were celebrations, as at Christmas time, pork appeared on the menu, and whatever the diet, it was safe. From these pans the food was ladled out into large covered basins to be carried to the wards or the nurses' dining room. The kitchen presented an image of supreme cleanliness and without doubt, it represented security for all who ate from there. It was usually an object of wonder to patients and visitors alike. During the years considerable improvements were made in the diet given to nurses and patients, especially in the quantity of protein food and vegetables. One benefit which resulted was that patients in the wards, and nurses, gained a knowledge of practical nutrition which they were able to use to teach others. Not all the introductions were accepted without a degree of protest, usually on the basis 'that we haven't been used to eat this' but ultimately the company of others who ate the new diet with enjoyment, resulted in acceptance. Mobile patients who chanced to pass the time of day with the cooks in the steam kitchen would be treated to a dissertation on the benefits of the new food and the knowledge that it could be grown or obtained in the villages would help to convince and hopefully start a new practice.

There was another kitchen which coped with food for the private wards and this more nearly represented a domestic scene with coal-fired stoves and ovens in which a 'European' diet was cooked.

The fourth requirement concerning the boiler was that it should produce 'sufficient steam under pressure to operate a large new electrical engine.' (Dr Roberts' terminology for a 30 Kilo watts electrical). This was probably the element which enabled Mr Arthur Lloyd Thomas to estimate the required size of the boiler. This generator was a steam enthusiast's joy, a Bellis and Morcom single cylinder high speed steam engine directly coupled to a 30 KVA DC dynamo working at 100 volts. This cost the sum of £383, a figure which they could afford. It was well looked-after and it shone and it sang and it operated without complaint for as long as it was possible to operate the hospital on Direct Current at 110 volts. With this steam-driven generator there was a very large accumulator, a battery, which was charged daily to light the hospital through the night after the major load was over and the generator was switched off. Elwin and Widrel, his brother, nursed this battery with great care, they straightened bent plates or renewed them, they made distilled water to top up the cells and everything shone. The fact that there were lights all around the buildings at night greatly encouraged the nurses and helped to keep away undesirable people. It also meant that at any hour of day or night emergency procedures could be carried out in the theatre or labour ward.

A common occurrence in Shillong, especially during the rains when there were tremendous storms, was for the municipal power lines to be interrupted and a whole segment of the town would be plunged into darkness. The policy of self-sufficiency behind Dr Roberts' plan ensured that storms did not cause breakdowns in the power supply or affect the Welsh Mission Hospital.

The fifth and last requirement was that 'the new boiler should be adequate to operate the New Steam Laundry Plant.' The new laundry system – two electrically-powered rotary washers, steam heated, with a drying cabinet which had mobile racks on which to hang clothes which then were dried by circulating air heated by steam pipes. This equipment cost £700. The final finishing of the clean linen was done with electric hand irons. All this was a very radical change from the former practices. In the very early days the clothes were all boiled in a large copper pan about three and a half feet in diameter, over a wood fire, then put through a large mangle and hung on clothes lines to dry which was often an impossibility during the rains. A later system had a large wooden drum into which the boiled clothes were agitated. On top of this sat a mangle. Final ironing, when necessary, was done with heavy charcoal heated smoothing irons. That old system was but a variant on the techniques used by the 'dhobies' who took domestic washing to the river bank, hung bedclothes or saris on lines to dry, or draped them over large wicker-work cones inside which were charcoal fires.

Why should a mission hospital have an up-to-date steam laundry? The reason was because Dr Roberts saw that there was no possibility of having linen supplies of acceptable degrees of cleanliness, whiteness and near sterility without such equipment. There was inherent economy and efficiency in this bold system, lives were saved by it. But there were still some people among the Liverpool Committee who felt that this money might have been better used for the preaching of the Gospel. This was Dr Gordon Roberts' equivalent of an alabaster box of ointment.

The end of this section about the boiler stated – "This installation has been a great success and all the needs mentioned above are now being most successfully met and considerable economy is being achieved. Coal from Cherra is used in the great steam generator and so, Cherra, apart from being the centre of theological activities, is bringing light, heat and other benefits to Shillong!"

Dr Roberts also installed a small automatic telephone system which was a great blessing as long as it worked, but mice and monsoons troubled it. It was a distinct advantage to have a call on a telephone when an emergency arose, rather than to have a breathless nurse knocking at the bedroom window and crying out the word "Shittom-trouble" and, sometimes dashing off without saying what the matter was or where it was being faced.

Mention was made by Dr Roberts of the Radium Room in the Mission Hospital. During late 1936, Dr Roberts had sent out an appeal for money to buy radium for the treatment of cancer cases. The appeal had been made both in Shillong and in Wales. In a letter to the Rev Oliver Thomas, the General Secretary of the Presbyterian Church of Wales Foreign Mission at the Liverpool office, dated 18-3-37, he stated that very little money had come for the Shillong Hospital Radium

Fund and at that stage only £600 had been raised in Shillong itself, of which most had come from the Government.[65] He pleaded that the campaign be promoted because he wanted some £4000 at least. At this time there was quite considerable opposition to Dr Roberts and the appeal, particularly from an ex-missionary who seemed to have a grudge against all medical missionaries. He asserted that the Radium Fund "was done to save the hospital, as cancer was of no account in India".[66] That opinion is reminiscent of the statement made when Dr Roberts first proposed to build a hospital in Shillong – *"that there was no need for a hospital. There was no surgery in the Khasi Hills"*.

Gifts however continued to come in and by 19 October 1937 enough had been received to order radium to the value of £2156. This was sent out from England by post and, apparently, it was not encased in lead for the journey, for we are told that it was delivered to Shillong by a postman in due course as a little packet. That indicates the low level of awareness of the danger of radiation in those days.

The radium was contained in hollow platinum needles of various lengths and doses from half-inch needles with half a milligram to three-inch needles containing ten milligrams. There were also inch-long tubes containing twenty milligrams which were fitted into special containers for the treatment of cancer of the uterus and cervix.

The radium was stored in a large safe which was loaded with blocks of lead so that the radium in a central 'cave' was surrounded by five inches of lead in every direction to guard against radiation. The radium room was an annexe to the main theatre. In it was a table with lead glass screens on which any necessary manipulations with the needles could be effected – each needle had to be threaded with strong cotton or silk threads or stainless steel wires so that they would not be lost when they were implanted in the patients' tissues.

Whenever radium was implemented, as in a cancer of the cheek or tongue, records were kept of the precise number of needles of each denomination used. After the needles had been implanted under anaesthesia, the patients were then housed in a small room with a locked door in one of the inner courtyards near the theatre, and the needles were counted daily until the end of the treatment. Dr Hughes remembered a man with a cancer of the tongue dealt with in this way, and when the count was made one morning during the course of his treatment, it was discovered that one needle was missing. Great was the alarm. The patient as blissfully unconcerned, but finally after much questioning, he reported that one needle had indeed become loose and he had pulled it free and pushed it into his mattress. The mattress was stuffed with pine needles, and it seemed to Dr Hughes that they were faced with a task as difficult as finding a proverbial needle in a haystack. It was found however after taking the mattress through the X-ray room and screening every inch of it with X-rays.

Dr Hughes also remembered a village woman who had a cancer of the cervix. The course of treatment consisted of the insertion of the applicators loaded with radium for twenty-four hours on three occasions separated by one week and then two weeks.[67] She was very intrigued by all this and asked about this strange *"medicine"*. It was explained to her that this "medicine" had been bought by women from Wales to help people just like her. *"Was it very expensive?"* she asked, and when she was told that it would have cost some three thousand Rupees she laughed with abandonment. When she stopped, she explained *"My whole body is not worth that much, but I have learnt that my soul is worth much more in the sight of Jesus my Redeemer,"* and she still laughed happily. She had been helped to that faith by what she had heard in hospital and especially from the nurses who had been dealing with her daily.

Much relief was given to many patients but, as in so much cancer treatment, remission was rarely achieved. In those days, radium was a more effective treatment than the X-ray therapy that was available. The nearest department which did practice deep therapy was in Calcutta and it was entirely out of the question that these Khasi patients could be sent to Calcutta to stay for a protracted course of treatment. The other limiting factor at all times was that the patients came when the condition had advanced too far for any hope of curative treatment. But in Assam in the 1930s and 1940s, radium represented the only specific treatment for cancers in the cases when surgery was not applicable.

The most striking statement made in the closing paragraphs of the Final Report refers to the contribution made by European patients' fees during the course of the years, namely that the total amount of fees from European patients which has been capitalised during the past twenty-nine years amounted to £23916/16/0, and represented approximately one third of the total cost of the hospital.

THE EVANGELICAL WORK IN THE HOSPITAL

In the brief biography of Dr Gordon Roberts in Nine Pioneer Missionaries written by his successor Dr Hughes, mention is made of the conflict which still remained in the minds of many missionaries, and of the Mission Committee (later called the Mission Board) in the early part of the century, concerning the relationship of the Medical Missionary's role to the work of evangelism.

Medical work performed by a missionary was regarded primarily as a means of securing a relationship with a patient which might result in conversion. The closeness of the relationship over what was often a prolonged period of time; the sense of gratitude possibly created by the act of service; the relief of pain and a ready sense of sympathy, all served to this end. The emphasis on a duty of compassion to the suffering was not often declared and it is quite evident that the idea of 'unconditional compassion' as a motive would surely not have been acceptable to the hard liners - at least not in theory. This implied that the medical missionary, or the totally unqualified missionary who ran a dispensary, should not waste his time treating a patient who showed not the slightest inclination to receive the Gospel, worse things than say, an untreated ulcer, awaited him in any case in the afterlife. Medical work was essentially a means to an end with these theologians. That generation of men and women faced illness and death in their own cases without any expectation of formal medical aid but only salvation and of eternal life. As medical aid became more effective there was a natural trend to change that hard line, but there was still the persistent expression of principle which made Dr Roberts, who had been ordained a Minister of Religion, protest time and again *"I am a missionary first and then a doctor"*.

Dr Roberts faced the challenge to evangelise as a preacher of considerable effectiveness to large gatherings, though his sponsors hardly expected him to do so when he was being considered as a missionary candidate. He preached in both English and Khasi.[68] His own theological position was warmly conservative and evangelical and his preaching bore this out every time. One friend within the Welsh missionary family with a much more liberal theological attitude said that he was glad *"that the drains which Dr Roberts installed were more up-to-date than his theology."*

The nurses in training were always guided spiritually by the missionary sisters in their classes and at appropriate times during their ward work. The attendance of the nurses in the services of the Jaiaw church, one hundred yards away from the hospital, involved them there in the teaching in Sunday School and in the week-night prayer or society meetings. The practice of the cottage meetings in the care of every church provided admirable training for young people.

They were in this way concerned for the spiritual well-being of the patients. In the days when there were a number of European patients in the hospital from tea-gardens or from the Civil Service, it was by no means infrequent to hear a comment from a patient during a ward round showing clearly enough that the Khasi nurses and doctors were concerned about their spiritual condition, and they managed to do this in so natural a manner that no embarrassment was ever caused.

Dr Roberts had a bitter experience with white ants destroying the timber of his buildings and this always remained a vivid reminder to him that mens' souls were equally vulnerable to inner decay. Many a time when he preached this simile was brought forward and he urged his hearers to be aware of this danger, and to be prepared to undertake the radical and painful steps to recover spiritual health. Decision for Christ was often the subject of his sermons and there was a phrase which often ended his plea for decision – that they might *"enter the service of the Master"* – spoken with an inflexion which was very characteristic of him.

For Dr Roberts himself, that phrase revealed an important aspect of his thinking. Obedience to a call to build a worthy hospital was inherent in his conviction, and he was determined that it should be no ordinary institution but the best that he and his friends could build. It was in that way that he could honour the Master. That he should have to build this hospital at a time of enormous change made the task the greater, but the fact that the accommodation and equipment stood up to the needs imposed by the years of the Second World War in the East and gave the opportunity to provide refuge and help to the hundreds of army patients who were accommodated there, of whom so many were from Wales, was a tribute to his imagination and boldness.

Sir Christopher Wren is memorialised in St Paul's Cathedral by an inscription which invites he who looks for a memorial to look around him. In a similar way it could be said that as a memorial to Dr Roberts nothing better could be imagined than to look around the buildings as they were in 1942 before the World War brought about a transformation in Assam, and medicine advanced at an unparalleled rate, changing the face of practice in such a way as to render the buildings out-of-date, and make some accommodation redundant. There never was such a time of change as the years which followed 1942.

When Dr H. Gordon Roberts retired from the hospital in 1942, a plaque was set up on the wall of the entrance to the private wards with the following inscription:[69]

THE KHASI HILLS WELSH MISSION HOSPITAL
this tablet was erected
to commemorate
the service of
The Rev Dr Hugh Gordon Roberts, CIE, MD
The Founder of the Hospital,
From 1922 to 1942 he gave invaluable service
as its Senior Medical Officer.
He was deeply sensible of the
suffering of the people, and this
fired his imagination to build and

develop this Hospital that it might
become an Institution responding to
great needs and within whose walls the
Great Physician might heal the wounds
of all who came for help.

In the brief biography to Dr H G. Roberts in Nine Pioneer
Missionaries, the chapter ends with the words:
"Building is evidence of Commitment."[70]

THE ASSISTANCE OF DR ARTHUR HUGHES AND MRS NANCY HUGHES

Nancy and Arthur Hughes arrived in Shillong on 1 March, 1939. It
was beautiful spring weather. They lived with Dr and Mrs Roberts in
their bungalow and nearly every day they went to see how the building
of the new bungalow was getting on. This was on a site separated from
Dr Robert's bungalow and the hospital by the Jaiaw Church. The
whole tenor of their days was marked for then by the chapel bells.
Mrs Nancy Hughes was not expected to work in the hospital. It had
been made quite clear when they first arrived that the doctor's wife
was better out of hospital than in. The nursing sisters had to have
their own place. And so Nancy Hughes began her apprenticeship
as a doctor's wife under the guidance of Mrs Roberts. There was
much to learn about household management in a new country with
different domestic hazards and customs. She learnt a great deal about
the missionaries from all over the mission field and their traditions

and the stories about the generation who knew the Khasi Hills in the last century; she learnt about the Khasis in their homes and in the church and went visiting many Khasi families who became her lifelong friends; and she learnt about the social relationships with the people who ran the Government. This last relationship was a means by which Nancy Hughes became a link with the women who ran the Red Cross in the town and who later organised supplies of dressings and comforts for the troops in Burma, and later still for the troops who were actually living in barracks, or in hospitals or convalescent camps in Shillong itself. From among them came the women who welcomed the refugees from Burma at the foot of the Burma Road and who manned the stations along the Assam Railway so that they could bring cheer to soldiers on ambulance trains as they made their slow progress from the border towards India. This same group of friends worked for flood relief or for refugees in camps on the borders, or to bring emergency aid in epidemics. Mrs Nancy Hughes, as one of the few in the Mission who did not have a *"job description"*, was the effective unofficial link between the Mission workers and the friends of the Red Cross. Many or most of these friends were the wives of officials in Government service - others were women whose husbands were in business in Calcutta who could not get back to England and all were desperately anxious to do what they could to help with humanitarian services and good causes. Thus Nancy Hughes cycled up to the town each morning and spent hours with the Red Cross, which very soon became a group representing nearly every community in the town. Nancy Hughes had a kind disposition and personality, generous and humble in her ways, walking in the paths of godliness, and it was easy for her to make friends and get everyone involved. Experience in this kind of work and the fellowship it created undoubtedly removed many social barriers to co-operation in kindly causes.[71]

Sunday was a day of bells for both of them, and each bell called someone to work. They started at seven o'clock, and Nancy Hughes taught first of all in the Jaiaw Church Sunday School and then in the English Sunday School in the church up in the town in the morning. Mid-morning the senior Sunday School classes met in the chapel, with overflow meeting for the various departments in different buildings. At one o'clock the preaching service started, followed by the women's meeting. In the evening there was a service in the English chapel with a mixed congregation of pupils from the high schools and colleges and Shillong residents and visitors. In this chapel that they called the *"English Service",* there were English-speaking schools held for English, Bengali, Naga Lushai youngsters, during the course of the day.

Dr Hughes was asked to teach classes for the Red Cross examinations which later developed into classes for auxiliary nurses for the Army. In those early days, life was very full of learning for the new surgeon: learning his way around the hospital; learning what could be done in the operating theatre; learning to get on with patients of many, many different tribes and tongues, and of course learning the language in two parts - there was what one learnt in hospital, all the words for pain and sickness and relief or comfort and the words of instruction to nurses, and at home at half past six in the morning, Primrose Gatphoh came to teach him formal Khasi and to prepare him for the First Khasi examination. There were Khasi readers, some of them prepared by the old missionaries, who were well versed in grammar as well as the Gospels. All of these classes had to be studied together with the traditional, conventional Khasi. Dr Hughes enjoyed it very much as he often told me and because his day was spent in the company of Khasi patients and nurses and doctors, he got all the practice he needed in the language. Because of this he was able to preach his first Khasi sermon in the Jaiaw Chapel in Shillong within nine months. Indeed when he came back to Liverpool in 1969 he still thought in Khasi; he had become a fluent speaker.

In the early days, Dr Roberts conducted Dr Hughes around the whole of the hospital buildings giving a running commentary about the then needs and the whole history of that particular section and his ideas of what should happen. They passed through the wards and the theatres and his X-ray department and the dispensary and the kitchens and the laundry. They visited the engine rooms and heard Elwin enlarging on the themes which Dr Roberts related. Then they came to a building which he announced was the mortuary, and he pointed to another building which he said was designed to be the new mortuary *"because he knew that I was coming he appreciated that there would be need for more accommodation."* His plans however had been upset because the people who lived nearest to that site objected to the use which would be made of the building so that they had to be satisfied with the old mortuary for the next thirty years.

Dr Roberts was never short of ideas about the next building which must be erected or alterations to existing buildings; many of the buildings had extensions and bulges and bits added here and there, changes which were very easily carried out with the old-fashioned timber-framed lath and plaster buildings. It was a style most suitable for *"arriere pense"* designing.

During the early part of 1940 all the Mission stations were involved in their turn in a project to record their activities on film as a propaganda effort for the Presbyterian Church back in Wales. Dr Hughes planned a wide ranging programme for the hospital and the work was done by a Mr Lionel Hodgson who was then the Secretary for the Bible Society in Calcutta. The film still exists and it does give a very good picture of the hospital, with glimpses of Shillong as it was over seventy-five years ago.

From Shillong the intention was to go on to Jowai some 34 miles away to film the district work there and the hospital. They took two days for the journey to Jowai, stopping the night at a dak-bungalow on the way. The missionary Rev Anthony Crockett who had left Shillong with them, left them there and continued on his way to Shangpung. Early in the morning of the third day a message came from Mrs Blodwen Crockett to say that she feared that her husband had developed appendicitis. Dr Hughes immediately left on a pony to see him, a journey of about fifteen miles. He confirmed after watching for an hour that Anthony Crocket indeed had appendicitis and it was arranged that he should be carried in to Jowai in a basket on a man's back. Therefore he travelled and reached Jowai late that evening. It was too late and Dr Hughes was too tired to do anything then. He arranged to resurrect as many instruments as they could from those in daily use and these, supplemented from an old post-mortem set represented the equipment.[72] The following morning in a theatre in which no surgery had been performed for years, the appendix of the dedicated missionary was removed, with Mrs Doris Blodwen Crockett giving the anaesthetic to her husband.[73] A telegram was sent to Mrs Nancy Hughes. The Jawai missionary Reverend Angell Jones went to meet her from Shillong with two ponies. Having met Angell Jones, she galloped all the way in style to Jowai. She was the first European woman to have done the journey from Shillong to Jowai on horseback in one day. Tony Crockett made a successful recovery and within a few weeks he was himself galloping on a pony to the Khasi villages on his pastoral and preaching engagements.

Dr Hughes was enthusiastic and grateful that he could build on the enviable reputation of the Welsh Missionary Hospital. He took charge of all the general wards, while his hero Dr Roberts was in charge of the administration and finance.

THE FIRST IMPRESSION OF DR R. ARTHUR HUGHES OF THE WARDS IN SHILLONG AND THE PATIENTS

In the first six months, Dr Hughes had an opportunity to recognise the differences between the experience of working in hospitals in Liverpool and the situation in Shillong.[74]

In the first place he expected to see at least the same clinical conditions in Shillong that he had been involved with in the Northern Hospital Liverpool, but he expected that the diseases would be more advanced and the patients in a worse condition. He also expected the pathology would be more advanced. The bias might be different, proportionately more of one thing than another even among the familiar conditions. One would then expect a number of patients with truly tropical conditions which one would not expect to witness in Liverpool. On the medical side, Dr Hughes expected to see more conditions with an infectious basis – the dysenteries, typhoid, typhus tuberculosis etc, and of course a large number of patients with malaria. In the event he did see all this but the acutely depressing fact was that among patients in Shillong who were categorised as suffering from chronic dysentery there seemed to be a high death rate.[75] These Khasi patients were often those who had the greatest problems with superstition. The treatment of these patients with *"chronic dysentery"* seemed to be totally ineffective and, lest one should forget them, as just another *"chronic dysentery"*, dying, he laid it down early and clearly that he must be called to be present night or day when such a patient seemed to be on the verge of dying so that he would not forget them and perhaps that he might see something significant which might give him some ideas for treatment. Certainly this experience made Dr Hughes the more concerned that the sphere of medical work should be extended to include the villages so as to see if they could reduce endemic diseases like dysentery, malaria and the like. He began to recognise the nutritional disorders; surprisingly enough, rickets was one of the commonest, and with infants and children, what later came to be called Kwashiorkor, and always anaemia and swelling and worms.

THE MATERNITY WARD

The almost total absence of any ante-natal care was immediately apparent to the young surgeon. This resulted in some horrifying problems in delivering even the small babies which were usual. When patients were brought from a distant village where a *"wise woman"* or a compounder had made unsuccessful efforts during the course of a long labour to deliver without success and especially if the baby was still alive, the fact of previous interference narrowed down the possible lines of treatment to the use of forceps because Caesarean sections in such conditions were precluded by almost inevitable peritonitis. Dr Hughes told me:

"It must be remembered that at that time we had no antibiotics in Shillong. Patients undergoing the classical Caesarean section were at risk of suffering fatal peritonitis.[76]

A few cases of rupture of the uterus would present as a consequence of interference and then there would be no choice – the baby would have to be extracted from the abdominal cavity – come what may."

Another category of cases which intrigued Dr Hughes was the young mothers not immunised to malaria, often with enlarged spleens and gross anaemia. They were expected to work hard. Her husband would be expected to work as hard as he could. He was an additional pair of hands to work the fields belonging to the wife's family.

The third category represented a pitiful group of women, oedematous and grossly anaemic, that is less than 10% of a normal haemoglobin level, who were in those early days nearly all sentenced to death. Any attempt to give such women a blood transfusion by the techniques then used would result in the patient's death.[77] Today we now know that this is due to the associated weakness of cardiac function in severely anaemic patients, in particular in patients with pernicious anaemia.

THE CHILDREN'S WARD

Dysentery and malnutrition was to be witnessed in the children's ward. Tuberculosis in every form, such as spinal or hip tuberculosis, tuberculous meningitis, grossly enlarged lymph glands in the abdomen, tuberculosis enteritis, and of course tuberculosis of the lungs. The disease of tuberculosis was so widespread that it was not surprising that within a month or two of his arrival Dr. Hughes was swept up into a campaign, initiated by the Government, to plan for a sanatorium in Shillong. He began his first piece of research in his new appointment by looking at comparing the frequency of tuberculosis in town and village populations. This interest in medical research continued all through the years. In due course when BCG vaccine became available, Shillong Hospital took part in popularising vaccination campaigns until they had routine immunisation of all schoolchildren and of the new-born as part of a modern package of childhood immunisation. He well remembers seeing his son John at five years of age, heading the queue of hostel children from the Mission school in a BCG inoculation drive, in order to encourage the rest.[78]

Malaria was usually present in any child from the Bhoi villages to the north of Shillong. The clinical history of the women in the maternity ward showed that twice as many young children born to mothers coming from Bhoi died compared with the deaths among children born to women from the people from the town of Shillong and from the villages on the grasslands at a higher altitude. Figures were collected over the years which stimulated Dr Hughes to start a scheme for the villages.[79]

ADULT SURGERY

It was especially in this field that he saw the conditions which could be seen in Liverpool in the 1930s, usually aggravated by anaemia and poor diet. Peptic ulcers were the commonest and many of these were complicated at the very least by anaemia and oedema. Then came gall bladder disease, a majority with stones and showing a tendency to appear at a younger age than usually associated with the condition, between an attack of typhoid or a severe dysentery and the beginning of the condition. He cultivated the typhoid germs from the heart of the gall stone in many an instance. The third group would possibly be the cases of advanced tuberculosis of the bowel; in the early days in Shillong, it was still possible to cure a good proportion of them by surgical operations, but in later years when antibiotic treatment became available, they were more effective in this field as with other tuberculosis conditions.[80]

ANAESTHETICS

One of the first problems which faced Dr Hughes as surgical work in the Welsh Mission Hospital increased was the provision of anaesthetics. At the David Lewis Northern Hospital in Liverpool where he had been surgical registrar, the surgeons had been blessed with the service of anaesthetic agents of the time, mainly Gas-and-Oxygen supplemented by a little ether; or *"open ether"* – ether dripped onto a mask or spinal anaesthetics.[81]

In Shillong at nearly five thousand feet and at temperatures often much higher than in England, open ether had to be supplemented with chloroform, two parts of ether to one of chloroform for the open technique. This almost ensured an unpleasant going to sleep and very difficult problems for the surgeon because relaxation was so difficult to achieve, especially with untrained anaesthetists. Many patients afterwards had a bad chest and vomiting. A further disadvantage was that with a shortage of staff it was often difficult to get an anaesthetist. As in many hospitals in Britain which depended on junior doctors, or none, for anaesthetics, surgeons came to rely on spinal anaesthetics which they administered themselves to the patient. There was a very limited choice of spinal anaesthetic agents available. Those in general use only allowed about forty minutes of operating time at the most.

Towards the end of the thirties, new agents appeared which could give much longer periods of anaesthesia and could be used safely even for upper abdominal operations. There were some hazards which had to be guarded against but in the main, spinal anaesthesia served very well for many cases and, above all, there was a much more peaceful induction and fewer chest complications. The text on the anaesthetic room wall written by Dr Roberts was *"I will lay me down to sleep in peace"* but an induction with open ether-chloroform often belied that statement. A spinal anaesthetic gave peace which enabled many a patient to take part in a prayer with the surgeon before starting the operation. This anaesthesia the Khasis referred to as puid-im, operate on the living, that is, a still-conscious patient.

The beginning of the War brought many supply problems; even spinal anaesthetic drugs became difficult to obtain, and Dr Roberts and Dr Hughes had to rely on using anaesthetic solutions made in the dispensary for elaborate methods of local anaesthesia, especially difficult for gall bladder or stomach operations.[82]

When the threat of war in the Far East became more serious, the medical journals which Dr Roberts had ordered, arrived once a month on a Saturday. Great were the expectations of both surgeons of the new and exciting medical advances when they opened up the journals. One Saturday the Lancet, to their great delight, printed three articles about a new piece of equipment called the "Oxford Ether Vapourizer (OEV)." This produced ether vapour at controllable concentrations which could be chosen to suit the case. This removed many uncertainties and difficulties about producing safe levels of anaesthesia. This apparatus had been invented by a team led by Professor Macintosh in Oxford, with the financial backing of Lord Nuffield, to meet the needs of military mobile hospitals as a portable self-contained anaesthetic machine. Both Dr Roberts and Dr Hughes thought that this would meet their needs perfectly. One of the team who reported on the clinical trials of this equipment was Dr Freda Bannister, who had been one of Dr Hughes's fellow students in Liverpool. By Monday morning Dr Hughes had prepared a letter to send to her asking if it was possible to obtain one of these OEVs. Dr Bannister replied stating that Lord Nuffield himself, who had funded the development of this apparatus, was going to send one to the hospital in Shillong. Great was their joy. In due course it came, in a handy black box with a shoulder strap, complete with an instruction book to detail the way it could be used.

Not long after the surgeons received the apparatus they were delighted to be able to greet Squadron Leader Hywel Roberts, a surgeon attached to an RAF mobile field hospital in the Arkaan. He was the son of one of the missionaries in the plains of Sylhet and was well-known to both Dr Roberts and Dr Hughes. He had come on a brief leave to Shillong. In course of time all the officers of that unit came to stay with them on leave. One of them was Flt Lieutenant Mitchell, their anaesthetist, who had also been a member of the same team testing the OEV. His arrival was a great blessing for he could give both Dr Roberts and Dr Hughes specific training in the use of the apparatus. One cannot imagine a more providential series of events.[83]

Even then there were problems. First the ethyl chloride which was used to speed up the induction went off the market, then even ether became unobtainable for a long time until an American source made it available in India. When no ether could be obtained they had to revert to the use of spinal anaesthesia or local block anaesthesia.

When the War was over and Dr Orientcey Roy had been released from the Army they were able to send her to Liverpool for a short course in the Department of Anaesthesia at the University of Liverpool, specifically to learn to use relaxants with the OEV. When she returned she could give anaesthetics for any kind of case using the OEV with ether, relaxants with intubation and air only.

At the Medical College in Assam Valley the anaesthetists were in great distress at times because they could not get any gas (nitrous oxide) or oxygen, all of which had to come from Calcutta, but in the Welsh Mission Hospital, they were in the happy position of being able to continue with their surgery unaffected by the lack of oxygen or gas because there was plenty of fresh air to be had for nothing in Shillong, and that was all they needed with the OEV.

It seems that the Welsh Mission Hospital was the first non-military hospital in India to use the original Oxford Ether Vapourizer and it was a great experience to most people who came to visit them in the early years of the War.

Dr Roberts had to buy oxygen cylinders and transport them to Calcutta for refilling; this meant spending more time on the road or on the ferry boats than in hospital and a return trip might take three months. Dr Hughes investigated a technique of producing oxygen electrolytically, passing a current of electricity through cells of water made more conductive with caustic potash. This produced oxygen at one end and hydrogen at the other. Oxygen was piped into a gasometer for distribution. Thus they secured for Shillong an apparatus which produced pure oxygen which served for some years. The oxygen from the gasometer was piped to the operating theatre and maternity ward theatre.

TYING KNOTS

The ability to tie safe knots is essential for anyone who operates, and the next question is always – what shall we use to tie them?

Dr Arthur Hughes always saw catgut used for sewing and tying knots

- catgut which was spooled on glass spools immersed continuously in an iodine spirit solution. When a length was required the theatre sister would draw the free end from the spool and cut off the desired length with sterile instruments and pass it briefly through a bowl of sterile water to wash off the potentially irritating iodine solution. The use of tubed catgut in various sizes was becoming commoner, but it was more expensive.

When Dr Hughes got to Shillong the older system was the one practised by Dr Gordon Roberts and tubed catgut was too expensive. There was a lot of wound sepsis and Dr Hughes decided quite soon that spooled catgut was part of the course. Catgut is not absorbed - it is digested by the white cells in the blood which gobble up foreign digestible material. This is part of the picture of acute inflammation which is seen where the catgut is being digested in a wound.[84] In some American publications of the time reference was made increasingly to the use of silk or even cotton ligature material with a debate about the use of absorbable or non-absorbable materials. Dr Hughes began to use silk with much satisfaction, but before long silk ligature material became unavailable. He then turned to cotton, that is black sewing cotton, sizes 30 and 60. He had to learn to be much more gentle when using these grades of cotton for tying or sewing. This also meant that he had to have better anaesthesia so that they could be much gentler. It was also better to tie individual knots rather than make a long run with a continuous thread and this rather slowed down suturing. With better anaesthesia and better relaxation much gentler handling was possible and wounds healed much better. The cost of suture material dropped, for cotton was only a fraction of the price of catgut, and it was always available in the market. Price and availability were most important. Much later the general use of unabsorable suture material became common and Dr Hughes was introduced to nylon (fishing line), and even to stainless steel, but for many years only black cotton thread was used in the Mission Hospital.

Dr Hughes took charge of all the general wards while Dr Roberts continued in charge of the private ward (which brought in essential finance to help the hospital to function) as well as of the running of the Hospital. When Dr Roberts retired completely from his responsibilities in the hospital in March 1943, Dr Hughes became the Senior Medical Officer, Administrator and Finance Officer.

Dr Roberts could not be allowed to enjoy any well-deserved retirement, for he spent two more years overseeing more building work: in particular, an extension to the Dinam Hall in Shillong. His retirement was recognised when he received the honorary degree of Doctor of Law from the University of Wales in April, 1946. It was a fitting tribute to an extremely hard-working medical missionary.[85]

NOTES AND REFERENCES

1. R. Arthur Hughes, 'Hugh Gordon Roberts' in J. Meirion Lloyd (editor), Nine Missionary Pioneers (Caernarfon, 1989), D. Ben Rees, 'Hugh Gordon Roberts (1885-1961)' in Vehicles of Grace and Hope: Welsh Missionaries in India 1800-1970, edited by D. Ben Rees, (Pasadena, 2002), 194-196. For Catherine (Katie) Roberts (1880-1966), ibid., 189.

2. Dr David Roberts (1788-1869) became 'long before his death, the chief Calvinistic Methodist elder in Anglesey; a serious man, frugal though not miserly, somewhat autocratic – in a way an incarnation of the rather dour older Methodism of the island'. See, R. T. Jenkins, 'Roberts family of Mynydd-y-gof, Bodedern, Anglesey' in The Dictionary of Welsh Biography Down to 1940, (London, 1959), 858-59.

3. See A. Lax, Mynydd-y-gof, or the History of a Welsh Calvinistic Methodist Family (Manchester, 1905). This was privately printed by the sixth son, Robert Roberts (1828-1916) in Manchester where he had been a businessman and an agent.

4. R. Tudor Jones, Faith and the Cross of a Nation: Wales 1890-1914, ed. Robert Pope (Cardiff, 2004), 290-336; R. B. Jones, Rent Heavens: The Revival of 1904 (London, 1931), 12-36; for the fourth campaign on Merseyside, see Geraint Tudur, 'Evan Roberts and the 1904-5 Revival' in The Journal of Welsh

Religious History, Volume 4:2004, 80-101, especially 91-2 for Liverpool and Birkenhead

5. E. D Jones, 'Hugh Gordon Roberts (1885-1961)' in The Dictionary of Welsh Biography 1951-1970, (London, 2001), 177.

6. Gordon Roberts had two cousins who became missionaries in China. His male cousin was Frederick Charles Roberts (1862-94), son of John Foulkes Roberts (1817-1902), who became Lord Mayor of Manchester in 1896-7. In 1887 Frederick Charles Roberts went to China at first to assist James Gilmour in Mongolia, but settling afterwards in Tien-tsin where he died in 1894. His sister Mary joined him there in 1888. Afterwards she took charge of the hospital named after her brother and died in 1933. See Bryson, Fred C Roberts of Tientsin.

7. H. Gordon Roberts met the Revd Robert John Williams (1857-1933), a pleasant, brotherly and kindly man, as his colleague Rev J. Hughes Morris called him on 13 October 1912. The General Secretary gave an account of his meeting to the Liverpool General Purposes Committee and hopes to 'secure his services'. For Rev R. J. Williams, see D. Ben Rees, 'Robert John Williams (1857-1933)' in Vehicles of Grace and Hope, ibid., 243-44.

8. H. G. Roberts offers himself to the Liverpool General Purposes Committee on 12 March 1913. Letters of recommendation were secured from his minister Rev J. D. Evans, R. C. Jones and

Professor Commer, and concerning Katie from Rev J. D. Evans on 16 April he was accepted by the Liverpool Directors and his cause was to be transferred to the General Assembly. Miss Katie Jones could not be present, therefore it was arranged for her and H. Gordon Roberts to a special meeting to be held on 30 April so has to commit then to the Lord in prayer. On 30 April 1913, H. Gordon Roberts and his fiancée Katie were introduced to members of the Finance Committee. On 6 May 1913 the Officers in Faulkner Street, Liverpool decided to ask the North Wales Association of the Presbyterian Church of Wales to ordain H. Gordon Roberts, if possible in the English language, rather than in the usual Welsh liturgy.

9. The General Purposes Committee on 23 July had decided to defer the location of the New Hospital until H. Gordon Roberts had reached Shillong. However, a member of his family, Mrs Foulkes Jones of Machynlleth, suggested that an appeal letter should be sent to the denomination's Welsh language weekly newspaper, Goleuad, asking for assistance to buy equipment. But the committee, whilst grateful for all such support, asked specifically that no public appeal be made. Mrs Foulkes Jones and Rev J. D .Evans had been gathering subscriptions. They were able to by personal contact with a few friends to collect the sum of £800. The Mission committee were reluctant for anyone to take their own initiative and decided that there was no need for a circular to plead the special merits of the case. Mrs Foulkes Jones had a large circle of friends and was always a generous supporter

of the missionary work.

10. They received the reply on 5 July 1913.

11. It is interesting to read of the voting among the missionaries on the location of the new hospital. On the north side of Shillong, seven voted in favour, including all the hills missionaries. Six voted on the southern side. At the second voting only 1 voted for Shillong and the plateau above while on the final voting, nine voted for the plateau above Shillong. E. H. Williams and Dr Oswald Williams dissented while D. E. Jones abstained. For E. H. Williams, see D. Ben Rees, 'Edward Hugh Williams (1865-1962) in Vehicles of Grace and Hope, 235-6; for Dr Oswald Williams, see D. Ben Rees, 'Oswald Osborne Williams (1868-1926), ibid., 242-3; for D. E. Jones, see J. Edward Jones, 'David Evan Jones (1870-1947) in Vehicles of Grace and Hope, 82-3. They took also the decision that Dr H. G. Roberts should take charge of Mawphlang District in 1914.

12. The Medical Committee in Liverpool considered rough plans for the hospital to be erected in the Khasi Hills to be further scrutinised by the Khasi Hills missionaries. The Finance Committee on 10 September 1913 agreed to the purchase of medical instruments for Dr H. Gordon Roberts as per list submitted by the Medical Committee. Then on 17 October the General Purposes Committee that met in Liverpool decided that the new hospital should be located in Shillong and Dr H. G.

Roberts to start work on its implementation as soon as possible.

13. NLW. Letter of H. Gordon Roberts to Rev R. J. Williams, dated 18 November 1913.

14. NLW. Letter of H. Gordon Roberts to Rev R. J. Williams, dated 2 December 1913, urgently in need of drugs. He expected to be able to pay for more drugs than he ordered as 'we shall make a small charge for each bottle.'

15. NLW. Letter of H. Gordon Roberts to Rev R. J. Williams, dated 8 December 1913. Still wanting drugs, and still looking for a suitable site. Suggests to the General Secretary that he should acquire a motorcycle, hoping then that he could visit fixed places on fixed dates without losing time on his missionary duties.

16. NLW. Rev H. Gordon Roberts wrote to Rev R. J. Williams from Shillong on 30 December 1913 stating that it had been very cold and he had caught a chill since Christmas day. He mentions how he had been to Cherrapunji and seen patients from morning to night. He still longed for the time when the Shillong Hospital would be an accomplished fact, but there was a great deal to consider in selecting the best site. This included the water supply, room for extension and a host of other matters. On 11 January, 1914 he mentions the death of the daughter of the Reverend C. Huxley Thomas and Mrs Thomas. For Huxley Thomas, see D. Ben Rees, 'C Huxley Thomas (1881-1974) in Vehicles of Grace

and Hope, 216. Revd. John Ceredig Evans, a headmaster in Shillong, was ill with typhoid. For J. C. Evans, see D. Ben Rees, 'John Ceredig Evans (1855-1936) in Vehicles of Grace and Hope, 40-41. The deaths of R. Dorka, of Rai Bhafur's daughter and his sister and later Rai Bhafur himself died.

17. In this meeting after careful consideration of several possible sites it was unanimously decided to build the new hospital on the Jaiaw Hill. J. Ceredig Evans and H. Gordon Roberts were authorised to start the collecting of materials immediately. A local building committee was to look after the plans with a number of missionaries, in particular E. H. Williams, J. Ceredig Evans, John M. Harries-Rees.

18. NLW. Letter of H. Gordon Roberts to Rev R. J. Williams dated 17 March 1914. Ceredig Evans was very depressed about the death of the Khasis. The site of the hospital was fixed in Jaiaw where Ceredig used to live before the earthquake. Ceredig Evans tells Dr Roberts that in the Earthquake Fund there is a certain sum of money which was especially given to defray the cost of rebuilding of the Cherra Hospital. On every hand he could see the need for action, and it was a great joy for him to be able to do some little service for those who suffer so much and through helping them physically, he could find a way to the heart of those who had never known of the Saviour's transforming love.

19. Treasury, August 1913

20. 5-5-1914

21. For the missionary doctors, Edward Williams, see D. Ben Rees, 'Edward Williams (1866-1925)' in Vehicles of Grace and Hope, 235 and Dr Griffith Griffiths, see D. Ben Rees, 'Griffith Griffiths (1852-1922)' in Vehicles of Grace and Hope, 55-6. Dr Griffiths resigned because of ill-health in the Spring of 1904, and accepted a call to the English speaking Presbyterian Church in Holywell, Flintshire.

22. See note 20.

23. NLW. Letter of Dr H. Gordon Roberts to Rev R. J. Williams, dated 17 November 1914. He informed the General Secretary of the Foreign Mission that he was ready to accept the post of a Civil Surgeon if offered a 50/50 salary.

24. The Liverpool General Purposes and Finance Committee gave permission to Dr H. G. Roberts to buy the car from Major Scott.

25. Letter of Dr H. G. Roberts to J. W. dated 22 June 1915.

26. For Beatrice Jones, see D. Ben Rees, 'Beatrice Jones (1888-1975)' in Vehicles of Grace and Hope, 77; Dr Gwyneth Roberts, 'Mrs Beatrice Jones, Pensarn, Abergele (late of Shillong)' [in] Presbyterian Church of Wales Year Book for 1976, 259.

27. NLW. Letter of Dr H. Gordon Roberts to Revd R. J. Williams. The future was difficult for the directors. Present earning of Dr Roberts will help to form a fund which will be of help in meeting the annual expenditure of the new hospital. The impact of Miss Beatrice Jones enabled him to continue with his operative work as a surgeon. Miss B. Jones had asked once if she could be transferred to the proposed Mission Hospital, but the government authority had proposed to build a house for her and her sister. It would therefore give offence to the government authorities if she asked to be transferred. In the letter he broaches the Mission Directors with the idea of having a bungalow next to the new hospital for himself and his family. He points out to the General Secretary that there will be no room in the existing Jaiaw Chapel for the congregation plus the patients and their families. Dr Roberts felt that it would be advantageous if the Foreign Mission of the Presbyterian Church of Wales is able to assist them in building a brand new chapel.

28. NLW. Letter of Dr H. G. Roberts to Rev R. J. Williams dated 4 January 1917. He maintains that he has used up all the money donated by the mission authorities plus equipment grant as well as the Government grant. Dr Roberts goes on to say that 'I am now using the money earned as Civil Surgeon'. It is not possible for him to get a holiday but he suggests that when the War is over that he comes back to Liverpool for a short furlough and study.

29. NLW. These letters of Dr H. G. Roberts to the directors of the Mission clearly indicates that he was under great stress and unable to get his own way. In a letter dated 14 March 1917 to the Directors stating that he should be allowed a short furlough because he had only ten days leave in the last two years. He would like to use his break to see the recent advances in surgery. Government would give Rs 2000 as a holiday bonus for him after three years' service. The Committee however could not see anyway of granting a short furlough and urged Dr Roberts to arrange local leave as soon as possible. In a letter on the same time to Rev R. J. Williams he enlarges on the theme of a District Committee minute on the scheme to build a doctor's house in Jaiaw. His present bungalow was too far from hospital, he wanted to be at hand for any emergency. On 18 April 1917 he mentions to the General Secretary his surprise that directors would not grant short furlough after the end of the War. He admitted that he was in an unsatisfactory state of health. If the directors cannot agree to his request he would like them to accept his resignation as from the date of letter, as he was now a Government servant. On 9 December 1917 in a letter to Rev R. J. Williams he underlines his regret and surprise that the directors in Wales and Liverpool do not agree now with his request and may ultimately be unable to grant on the grounds that it doesn't accord with regulations. Since the work with the Government takes up all his time and he can give very little effort to the Mission he feels that it is only reasonable that he should operate temporarily under the Government regulations. In this letter he asks to be released from

the service of the Welsh Mission until after the conclusion of the First World War. The directors replied to him on 12 December, agreed to his request, paying regard to the clause that stated that at the completion of three years' service there would be a final payment on account of leave. They agreed to the request hoping that his return would be a help to devote himself entirely to the missionary work after the War is ended.

30. NLW. Letter dated 10 December 1918, of Dr H. G. Roberts to Rev R. J. Williams. He admits that 1918 had been the heaviest year yet, but he was delighted that the main building of the new hospital was now completed. However, more than Rs 15000 is still needed for the building of the isolation ward, out buildings and the installation of electricity. To please directors, he stated that after five years in India 'I am convinced that I am a missionary first and a doctor afterwards'. But then he adds that he would like permission to build a new bungalow.

31. NLW. A letter was received from Dr Roberts dated 15 January 1919 in regard to the new hospital and a new bungalow for himself. The committee proposed that a sympathetic letter be sent to Dr Gordon Roberts approving his suggestion to approach Government for a further grant towards the new hospital and suggesting that no steps be taken regarding the new bungalow until he returns home.

32. This important letter has been reproduced from the Dr R. Arthur

Hughes file in my possession as Director of the North West India-Wales Trust.

33. Letter from Sir Beatson Bell, re: grant, in March 1919.

34. NLW. Letter from the Liverpool General Committee dated 16 April 1919, which pleased Dr Roberts, and that nearly Rs 100,000 had come to the Welsh Mission Fund through the efforts of Dr Roberts. The chairman proposed that the Welsh Mission declared their great appreciation of Dr Roberts' service and his incomparable generosity in connection with the new hospital in Shillong.

35. D. Ben Rees, 'Hugh Gordon Roberts (1885-1961) in Vehicles of Grace and Hope, 195

36. Revd J. D. Evans was a faithful adviser and friend to Dr Gordon Roberts. For J. D. Evans, see J. Elwyn Jenkins, 'James Daniel Evans (1870-1936) in Vehicles of Grace and Hope, 39-40.

37. ibid,40

38. For her life and achievements, see Menna Phillips, 'Miss Margaret Elizabeth Buckley, 1897-1941', in J. Meirion Lloyd (ed.), Nine Missionary Pioneers (Caernarfon, 1989), 38-43; D. Ben Rees, 'Margaret Elizabeth Buckley (1897-1941)' in Vehicles of Grace and Hope, 9-10; National Library of Wales, CM Archives, the M.

E. Buckley papers; D. Ben Rees, 'Miss M. E. Buckley and the Birth of Professional Nursing in Assam' in the Journal of Welsh Religious History, New Series, Volume 5, 2005, 77-86.

39. Margaret Buckley worked long hours as a nurse, on one occasion going for 72 hours without sleep. D. Ben Rees, ibid., 79.

40. D. Ben Rees, 'Margaret Elizabeth Buckley (1887-1941)', ibid., 9.

41. For Revd J. Hughes Morris, the historian of the Mission, editor of the Cenhadwr (Missionary) and Glad Tidings, see D. Ben Rees, 'John Hughes Morris (1870-1953) in Vehicles of Grace and Hope, 150-1. The article of Dr H. Gordon Roberts appeared in the Treasury.

42. NLW. Letter of Dr H. Gordon Roberts to Rev R. J. Williams dated 20 December 1921. He felt wonderfully well though the strain of the work was considerable as he admitted all through the year. He indicated his concern about the cost and expense of completing the sanitation scheme. It was a huge sanitation scheme. He could not defer the building because this would have necessitated bringing up the sanitary engineers, as well as the electricity experts all the way from Calcutta. He had his eye on Dr Homiwell Lyngdoh, the first Khasi to graduate as a medical doctor from the University of Calcutta, as an assistant surgeon. But he felt that Dr Lyngdoh would require Rs 4-500 at least as a salary. As it happened, Dr Lyngdoh served the Government from 1902 until his retirement in 1932, and was the first Secretary of

the Presbyterian Assembly of Khasi-Jaintia. For Dr H. Lyngdoh, see D. Ben Rees, 'Homiwell Lyngdoh (1877-1958) [in] Vehicles of Grace and Hope, 125-6; also M G Lyngdoh, 'A tribute to Dr H. Lyngdoh' [in] Recapture (Shillong, 1992), 69-73.

43. NLW. Letter of Dr H. G. Roberts to Rev R. J. Williams, dated 10 January 1922.

44. NLW. Letter of Dr H. G. Roberts to Rev J. Hughes Morris, dated 17 January 1922. In this letter he mentions how the hospital is costing three times more than was originally estimated. He hopes that Major David Davies of Llandinam will come to the rescue. He was finding it difficult to know how to approach him with the request for money. Dr Roberts regrets that no-one can come to help with the finances. At this time he was also involved in dealing with the mission accounts due to the illness of Revd E. Hugh Williams. These responsibilities meant the neglect of many patients whom 'under present circumstances I cannot possibly find the time to treat.' The medical work to his great regret had to suffer. By 7 March he sent the account to Liverpool. He also informed the office that he was too busy with the medical work and supervising the hospital building to be involved as local treasurer. The expected a great deal from him.

45. NLW. Letter of Dr H. G. Roberts to Rev R. J. Williams on 8 February 1922. He mentions that the opening ceremony would be held on March 25 when the Legislative Council was in session.

46. Dr Gordon Roberts sent a letter to the office after the opening ceremony maintaining that it was a huge success and that the Governor had given Rs 5000.

47. NLW. Dr H. Gordon Roberts to Revd R. J. Williams dated 20 June, maintains that the Miss M. Buckley was in danger of breaking down if she has to continue to work at such pressure. On 8 August he wrote to say that there were 16 Indian nurses in training which could look after 40 inpatients. But he reminds the officers in Liverpool that Miss Buckley was working much too hard. Her workload was huge. She stored the linen which arrived for the hospital direct from Wales. She set up beds and cots; filled cupboards with instruments; stuffed mattresses with soft pine needles; arranged for new accommodation for the nurses that came to her and she organised kitchens for the preparation of food for patients and for the nursing staff.

From the beginning she started to recruit girls to become nurses, girls prepared to accept the discipline she had undergone herself in the Brownlow Hill Infirmary in 1910. (See the testimonial of Martha Corbishley, Lady Superintendent of Nurses, Brownlow Hill Infirmary, Liverpool in National Library of Wales, CM Archives, the M E Buckley papers). It was not a question for Miss Buckley of choosing the most suitable from among a group of well-educated girls, but rather of persuading any girl who looked strong and alert, to join her. Some of the girls had received a middle school education in the Mission Schools and had gained a smattering of English. Others, however, were much less qualified.

Among the first were a few girls who had been carrying sand and stones for the builders working on the hospital compound. Some of these girls were barely literate, but Miss Margaret Buckley cared for them, taught them to read and studied the Bible with them, training them in the skills of hygiene and teaching them to understand the Khasi as well as the English languages. She did her best to imbue them with her own sense of Calvinistic devotion.

48. Finance was a constant problem for Dr H. Gordon Roberts. As he admitted in a letter to the office dated 10 October 1923, private patients' fees were crucial for the survival of the hospital. He admitted that private patient fees, especially European fees, had increased Rs 500 in three months. On 12 March 1923 he reminds the General Secretary and the Directors that in addition to £3000 already handed over to the hospital funds 'I have a further sum of money which represents earnings for the last year or so during which I acted as Civil Surgeon in Shillong. You will remember that during this period I did not draw any salary from the Mission. It may be fairly argued that I had a right to the money earned during the last year, but on the other hand I believe that my decision to hand this over to the hospital will meet with the approval of the directors. At the same time I hope that the directors will not be opposed to the control of this money being very largely in my hands, if that should be necessary, at any subsequent date. Owing to profit on exchange and accumulation at compound interest, the sum is not far from double what it was originally and stands at £4000.

49. Annual General Meeting for 1926 of the Assam Branch of the British Medical Association. See D. Ben Rees, The Medical Missionary Work of the Presbyterian Church of Wales in India, Vehicles of Grace and Hope, pps 129-136. The reference to this meeting is on page 134.

50. Simon Commission was designated after the name of its chairman Sir John Simon. The Commission which included the Welsh Labour MP, Vernon Hartshorn, were sent to India to study the constitutional issues. Their tour of India lasted from 11 October 1928 to 13 April 1929.

51. NLW. Letter of Dr H. G. Roberts to Revd R. J. Williams dated 18 January 1926 detailing the visit of the Viceroy with Sir John Kerr. The Viceroy was impressed and he stated:

'I was greatly impressed by what I saw and heard of the Khasi Hills Welsh Mission Hospital. I am filled with admiration for the great enthusiasm, energy and business capacity shown by Dr H. Gordon Roberts of the Welsh Presbyterian Mission in collecting funds to establish and maintain the mission hospital which is unique in many ways in the Indian Empire and for the high degree of scientific attainments which have made this hospital and his name, household words, both throughout Assam and outside the Province also.

I need not dwell on many exceptional attractions which the hospital provides in connection with the relief of suffering or upon the extensive nature of the equipment. I leave those features without apprehension as regards the verdict to the judgement of experts in the essentials of hospital management. I apply my own tests and after my visit I came away deeply impressed by the extent of the good work done here, by the patent cheerfulness and contentment of the patients here and the obvious general efficiency of the arrangements and the staff.

    ' 'The Viceroy sent a cheque for Rs 1000 to Dr Roberts. Sir John Henry Kerr (1871-1934) was Governor of Assam from 1922 to 1927.

52. Sir Laurie Hammond served for over 40 years in India, and succeeded Sir John Kerr as Governor of Assam in 1932. See 'Sir Laurie Hammond (1973-1939), Glasgow Herald, January 30, 1939, 13. When Sister Buckley had an operation in 1931 she received care in the Government House, in the home of Sir Laurie Hammond and Lady Hammond.

53. Gwalior was the fifth largest princely state in India. Situated in Madhya Pradesh. The Maharani of Gwalior was the wife of the ruler. An event like this established the reputation of Dr Roberts as a surgeon. See R Arthur Hughes, 'The Rev Hugh Gordon Roberts, CIE, MD, (Liv), Ll.D. (Wales), (1885-1968) [in] 75th Anniversary 1922-1997, Their Vision: Our Legacy, 43-4.

54. Dr Henry Hougton said of the Shillong Hospital:
'There is no hospital that I have seen in any mission field that comes nearer to the aim to give everything that is best by Western

Christians to the needy people of the East, nor expresses more purely the spirit of the Gospel as it is shown in the ministry of healing the sick. It is a place that gives inspiration to a person to visit and I came away with a new vision of the unbounded power that is in the Christian mission'. See Gwen C. Evans, 'An Appreciation of Dr R. Arthur Hughes' [in] 75th Anniversary 1922-1997, Their Vision: Our Legacy, ibid., 90.

55. General Sir John Stuart Mackenzie (1869-1966) was a British officer in the Indian Army. He retired in 1932 as General Officer Commanding-in–Chief, Eastern Command, India after four years in the post.

56. She was not successful with every Khasi nurse that came, but she trained enough young women in her ways to make a notable contribution to nursing in Assam, and thus enabled Dr Gordon Roberts to establish the hospital in Shillong as an institution where reliable treatment and care was available to meet the needs of all sorts of cases. See D. Ben Rees, 'Miss M. E. Buckley and the Birth of Professional Nursing in Assam, India' [in] The Journal of Welsh Religious History Volumes: 2005, 80.

57. D. Ben Rees, 'Amy Katherine Bullock (1889-1986)' in D. Ben Rees (ed.) Vehicles of Grace and Hope: Missionaries in India 1800-1970 (Pasadena, 2002), 10.

58. Between 1930 and 1934 there was a great deal of disagreement

between Dr Gordon Roberts and Margaret Buckley over the nature of training of nurses. Because of the tension between her and the Medical Director, she volunteered to go to another Welsh Presbyterian Hospital in 1934, known as Jowai Hospital. She became known in Jowai as Merecpang 'a mother looking after the sick'. See D. Ben Rees, 'Miss M. E. Buckley and the Birth of Professional Nursing in Assam, India', ibid., 84-5.

59. Miss Buckley threw herself into the task without any hesitation, training local girls, just as she had done in Shillong, to become nurses and encouraging her friends in Wales to collect funds as well as clothes to re-furnish the sadly neglected Jowai Hospital, ibid., 85.

60. We find an endearing portrayal of Miss Buckley in the world of nursing in the reminiscences of her fellow Welsh missionary nurses, such as Mary Hopkins, Menna Phillips (née Jones) and Helen Angell Ellen Jones (née Harris). See Nurse Hopkins, 'Ysbyty Shillong' in Y Cenhadwr, IV/8 (August 1925), 150-151; Angell Jones (Jowai), 'Er Cof Nyrs Buckley' in Y Cenhadwr, XX/5 (May 1941), 85-6.

61. D. Ben Rees, 'Robert Arthur Hughes (1910-1996)', The National Library of Wales, Welsh Biography Online; idem., 'Robert Arthur Hughes (1910-1996)' in Vehicles of Grace and Hope, 66-69; idem., 'Robert Arthur Hughes, OBE, FRCS' [in] 75th Anniversary 1922-1997. Their Vision, Our Legacy, The KJP Synod Hospital,

Shillong, formerly known as the Khasi Hills Welsh Misson Hospital, (Shillong, 1997), 51-55; idem., 'Dr R. Arthur Hughes', The Independent, 17 June 1996, idem., 'The doctor with a mission', The Guardian, 14 June 1996; T. Cecil Gray, 'Robert Arthur Hughes', British Medical Journal, Volume 313, 3 August 1996.

62. An interview with Dr R. Arthur Hughes at his home in Liverpool, November 2, 1979. Some of this appears in his appreciation of Dr H. Gordon Roberts, but not in the details I was given. See R. Arthur Hughes, 'The Rev Hugh Gordon Roberts, CIE, MD (Liv), LLD (Wales), 1885-1961' [in] 75th Anniversary 1922-1997. Their Vision, Our Legacy, The KJP Synod Hospital, Shillong, formerly known as the Khasi Hills Welsh Misson Hospital, (Shillong, 1997), 31-50, and especially page 43.

63. NLW. Letter to the Directors by Dr H. Gordon Roberts, Shillong, dated 10 August 1942.

64. R. Arthur Hughes, 'Mrs Menna Phillips, SRN, SCM, Shillong Hospital, Cherrapunji and Eglwysbach' [in] 75th Anniversary 1922-1997. Their Vision, Our Legacy, ibid., 66-7. She joined, in 1937, Miss Amy Bullock and Miss Doris Jones, 'and acquired the Khasi language by hard work and study in the early mornings and could use it with great freedom – something most necessary in her work'. She was an exceptional nurse as Dr Hughes maintains:

'Menna took her part in this teaching from the beginning of

her career in Shillong and the nurses were seen to mature very rapidly in knowledge, in understanding and in skills during these very critical years', 66.

65. NLW. Letter of Dr H. Gordon Roberts to Rev Oliver Thomas, Liverpool dated 18 March 1937. For Oliver Thomas, see D. Ben Rees, 'Oliver Thomas (1887-1950)' [in] 75th Anniversary 1922-1997. Their Vision, Our Legacy, 222-3; Revd Oliver Thomas, BA, The Yearbook of the Presbyterian Church of Wales 1951, 270-1.

66. NLW. Letter of the Rev Oliver Thomas to Dr H. Gordon Roberts dated 13 April 1938.

67. A private conversation with Dr R. Arthur Hughes after an elders meeting in Bethel Presbyterian Church of Wales, Heathfield Road, Liverpool in 1989.

68. See Rev H. Gordon Roberts, MB, BCh, 'Shillong, Meditation: Looking Back and Looking Forward: The Open Door' (presented at the Assam Medical Conference, Jorhat, November 1949) [in] 75th Anniversary 1922-1997. Their Vision, Our Legacy, 95-97.

69. R. Arthur Hughes, 'The Rev Hugh Gordon Roberts, CIE, MD (Liv), LL.D. (Wales), (1885-1961)' [in] 75th Anniversary 1922-1997. Their Vision, Our Legacy, ibid., 50.

70. This article was republished in 75th Anniversary 1922-1997.

Their Vision, Our Legacy, The KJP Synod Hospital, Shillong, 31-50.

71. For Nancy Hughes, see D. Ben Rees, 'Ann Beatrice (Nancy) Hughes (1908-2005)' [in] Vehicles of Grace and Hope, ibid., 61-2.

72. For Rev T. A. Crockett, see Raymond W. J. Welsh, 'Thomas Anthony Crockett (1905-1995)' [in] D. Ben Rees (ed.), Vehicles of Grace and Hope: Welsh Missionaries in India 1800-1970, (Pasadena, 2002), 13-14.

73. For Doris Crockett, see Raymond W. J. Welsh, 'Doris Blodwen Crockett (1904-1997)' [in] Vehicles of Grace and Hope, 13. She had been interested in nursing as a young girl in the Manchester Welsh community and when, in 1918, Dr Gordon Roberts toured Wales and the Welsh communities in England to appeal for help in building a hospital in Shillong. Doris Jones would stand in the chapel porch collecting the members' subscriptions.

74. An interview with Dr Hughes at his home in Liverpool in 1984 after he and Mrs Hughes had visited Shillong to advise on problems that had risen in the hospital where Dr Hughes had been the anchor. See D. Ben Rees, Labour of Love in Liverpool: The history of the Welsh congregations in the Chapels of Smithdown Lane, Webster Road, Ramilies Road, Heathfield Road and Bethel, Liverpool (Liverpool, 2008), 164.

75. The interview with Dr R A Hughes in 1984.

76. Ibid.

77. Ibid.

78. Ibid.

79. Ibid.

80. Ibid.

81. Ibid.

82. Ibid.

83. Ibid.

84. Ibid.

85. As Dr R. A. Hughes said of Dr Hugh Gordon Roberts in his splendid biographical article:

'Providence had certainly been very kind to him, and he had taken the fullest advantage of these gifts, but it must be appreciated that had he not the blessing of the dedicated labours of Miss Buckley and Miss Bullock in his time to train nurses, his service to the community would have been of a different order'.

Dr Hughes adds:

'He continued to build and alter and equip. His furloughs were used to present with fervour the case for support for the Shillong Hospital and his reputation as a missionary doctor never failed to draw the crowds. When the Second World War began, and fighting extended to the East and to Burma at India's borders the time came when this hospital proved its worth to an ever wider hospital.'

See R Arthur Hughes, 'The Rev Hugh Gordon Roberts, CIE, MD (Liv), LLD (Wales), (1885-1961)' [in] 75th Anniversary 1922-1997. Their Vision, Our Legacy. The KJP Synod Hospital, Shillong, ibid., 44.

THE AUTHOR: DAVID BENJAMIN REES.

Reverend Dr D. Benjamin Rees (known as D. Ben Rees) is one of the foremost historians on the missionaries from Wales who ministered in India and especially those who laboured in North East India from 1840 till 1970. Educated in the University College of Wales, Aberystwyth, the United Theological College in Aberystwyth, the University of South Wales in Cardiff, University of Liverpool and the University of Salford ,he was ordained in 1962 by the Presbyterian Church of Wales. Ever since he has been a dedicated, fully committed Minister of the denomination, He was a full time minister for 45 years and for the last 8 years he has been a part time minister, a distinguished witness in Wales and Merseyside as a powerful preacher , a caring pastor , inspired teacher, sought after lecturer, well-known scholar for the last 53 years. Born in the land of the Calvinistic Methodist Revival of the eighteenth century ,mid Ceredigion especially Llangeitho (where he was ordained in October 1962) and Llanddewi Brefi (where he was born and brought up in the faith by his parents Ann Jane and John Rees and his grandfather David Benjamin) , he has immersed himself in the life of the missionaries of North East India. for thirty years. His best missionary entries, hundreds of them, is seen in Vehicles of Grace & Hope: Welsh Missionaries in India 1849—1970 (Pasadena, William Carey Library) which he edited in 2002.He has written extensively in the Welsh Language as well on the Welsh missionaries. His portraits of his elder Dr R .Arthur Hughes (1910- 1996) is a source of inspiration to young people in Shillong and in Liverpool. In the city of Liverpool he has ministered for the last 47 years .His apprenticeship was served among the miners of the Aberdare Valley in South Wales. His involvement in the Aberfan Disaster in East Glamorganshire in 1966 has been well documented.. Married with two sons and two grandsons he is the Secretary and Director of research of the North East India Wales Trust since its foundation in 1995. It was established in Bethel Presbyterian Church of Wales, Heathfield Road/Auckland Road, Liverpool 15 as the result of the generosity of Gwyn Phillips of Ystrad Mynach and his family ,a brother of the lovable missionary, Reverend T.B. Phillips. (1898-1991).

J.Tikman. G.R.Handy. L.Tachuck.   R.An L.R.Chaporra. R.Al. Gierun-Nimbe. L.L.Humbles A.B.Weir W.N.Stirling.

A.G.Hemsley. R.Sinclair. M.A.Z.Fanili. G.E.S.Stewart. J.R.S.Innes. G.P.Jones. H. M'Gladdery. B.B.G.Nehaul C.S.C.Phiris R.H.Neeve. C.C.Wannesinha. S.S.Enshadi.

N.D.P.Kemeni A.K.Chowdhuri. B.C.Fountaine W.M.Fernando. G.P.Roberts. H.Demey.   R.Maarbis I.Gibbins M.S.Patrick G.A.Armstrong. L.T.Allen.

Sir Malcolm Wallen, Lady Wallen

London School of Hygiene and Tropical Medicine.
July.   1938.

Dr R. A. Hughes and the nurses of the hospital in Shillong

Standing L. to R. Dr. S. C. Doss, Dr. A. Cheshire, Dr. H. N. Roy, Dr. R. A. Hughes, Dr. T. Norman, Dr. W. D. V. Burton, Dr. T. W. Poole, Dr. D. Sarma, Dr. J. E. B. McPhail and Dr. A. S. Arora.

Sitting L. to R. Dr. D. A. H. McNaught, Dr. D. G. Cheshire, Lt.-Col. W. H. A. Thorne (Honorary Secretary), Dr. A. Gilroy (President), Lt.-Col. M. N. Khanna, Dr. A. R. Ray, Dr. J. V. Webster and Dr. L. Oswald.

Dr Gordon Roberts with his colleagues

The wedding of Rev T.B.Phillips and Sister Menna Jones in Shillong

Dr Roberts and Dr Hughes and the medical and missionary families

Dr Hughes as leader of the Welsh exiles
at the National Eisteddfod of Wales in Llandudno1963

Elders of Bethel Presbyterian Church of Wales, Heathfield Road, Liverpool 1982.
Standing J.Gwyndaf Richards, T.M. Owens, H.Wyn Jones, Glyn Davies, E. Goronwy
Owen, Dr John G.Williams, J.Medwyn Jones, Hugh John Jones
Sitting Miss Nina Hughes, Miss M.B.Owen, Dr R.A Hughes, Rev Dr D. Ben Rees, Mrs
Bronwen Rogers, His Honour John Edward Jones, W.Elwyn Hughes.

APPENDIX 1

HUGHES, ROBERT ARTHUR (1910-1996)

A medical missionary in Shillong, India and an influential Welsh Presbyterian Moderator. Born, he and his twin John Harris Hughes at Oswestry on 3 December 1910, the sons of the Reverend Howell Harris Hughes and his wife Mrs Annie Myfanwy Hughes (nee Davies), a native of Garth, near Llangollen who served as a headmistress in Rhosllanerchrugog. The family soon moved to Bangor and in the Garth School, both sons, had most of their elementary education. From Tabernacle Chapel Bangor the father received a call to the Welsh chapel of the Presbyterians at Waterloo in north Liverpool, and they received their education at Christchurch School in Seaforth (1921-1925) before moving to Llandudno and the John Bright School.

He had a distinguished period as a medical student in the University of Liverpool from 1928 to 1933, and he was one of the ablest students of his generation. He received the Gold Medal for surgery as well as other awards. Appointed a surgeon under Mr (later Professor) O Herbert Williams as well as an assistant to Dr (later Professor) Norman Capon at the Royal Southern Hospital.

He was invited to be the John Rankin Fellow in Human Anatomy at the University before serving for two years at the David Lewis Northern Hospital as a tutor and surgical registrar, before he offered his services as a medical missionary on the Khasia Hills in North East India. He was accepted by the Missionary Board of his denomination and he decided to equip himself further by gaining a Diploma in Tropical Medicine and further training at the Radium Institute and

Mount Vernon Hospital in London.

At the David Lewis Northern Hospital in Liverpool he met a nursing sister Nancy [Ann Beatrice] Wright of Heswall, who became his wife on 7 January 1939. Both then sailed on 28 January 1939 from Birkenhead to Calcutta. He began his lifework on St David's Day 1939 at the Welsh Mission Hospital in Shillong as assistant to Dr H. Gordon Roberts. He took responsibility for all the wards, with Dr H G. Roberts in charge of the administration until his retirement in 1942. Then Dr R A Hughes became the Senior Medical Officer, the administrator, as well as the finance officer. He gave substantial medical assistance to the wounded on the Kohima to Diampur – the famous Burma Road – comforting the refugees who were in desperate conditions escaping from the Japanese soldiers. Between 1942 and 1945 he dealt with thousands of soldiers and officers from all over the world, including a substantial number of Welsh soldiers who had to be treated in the Shillong hospitals. Dr R Arthur Hughes became the liaison medical officer, between the British Army and the local authorities in the Assam region.

Under his guidance the Welsh Mission Hospital of Shillong became one of the most important hospitals in the Indian sub-continent with patients flocking for treatment. Among these patients there were Government Civil Servants, entrepreneurs from the tea plantations of the Assam plain as well as Cachar including their families, and middle class people from as far as Calcutta. These patients were the chief source of finance for the hospital, allowing him and the staff to offer high medical and surgical care and opportunities for the poor Khasi folk who often would walk on foot 100 miles one way to receive treatment.

His daily schedule was long, twelve hours a day from Monday and Friday as well as a clinic on Saturday mornings. On Tuesday and Thursday he would be involved in the hospital from 7.30 in the morning until 10.30 at night. His surgical assistants were few, and he never had help from a medical person, while he was on the mission field, belonging to the Connexion though he made a number of pleas. He realised that the only answer as to train the Khasi nation to do the work. This was an important contribution of Dr R Arthur Hughes.

He was a pioneer in North East India who achieved remarkable change through his pamphlets fro public health and his initiative in tackling diseases such as malaria and typhoid. He began an extensive research to the medical condition of inaccessible villages in the Bhoi area, and persuaded the authorities in Delhi to sustain a campaign to conquer malaria. Dr Hughes established an itinerant pharmaceutical service with a jeep visiting the markets in the towns within reach of Shillong.

He gave substantial service to the Presbyterians in Shillong, and on Sunday he and his wife were heavily involved. Elected an elder in 1944 he was involved in religious education. In his work he was extremely caring for the needs of his fellow missionaries when they were ill, as well as missionaries belonging to other nationalities and churches. His son John brought joy to the home, and he also followed the footsteps of the family as a medical practitioner and in 2007 was ordained as an Anglican priest in Cheshire.

A farewell service to him and Nancy Hughes was held on 16 May 1969 when the Khasi hill people came to pay their tribute to one who was known as Schweitzer of Assam. He returned to Shillong in 1984 as well as in 1991 on the birthday of the church (150 years), and he had the opportunity of addressing a huge crowd reckoned to be 150,000 strong.

Dr R. A. Hughes made his home in 1969 in Liverpool, a city where his father had been born, and where his grandfather and the family lived in the Dingle in the nineteenth century. Appointed as Academic Sub-Dean of the Medical Department of the University of Liverpool in 1969, he retired in 1976. He gave sterling service to the Presbyterian Church of Wales, elected an elder at Heathfield Road Chapel, Liverpool 15 in 1971, became Moderator of the Liverpool Presbytery, Chairman of the Elders' Meeting of the North Wales Association in 1982-3, and Moderator of the General Assembly in 1992-3. Considering that he suffered from angina, he never missed a committee during his year of office, or an invitation to visit other denominations and churches. Though he had a weak speaking voice and as he admitted was much more fluent on his feet in the Khasi language than in Welsh or English, he made himself an endearing leader. Like his father before him he was a convinced absolute pacifist who took an abiding interest in the Peace Movement. He served as a trustee of the North East India-Wales Trust, and his contribution was always positive and useful.

He died on Saturday morning, 1 June 1996 at the Cardiothoracic Hospital, Broadgreen, Liverpool and the funeral service took place at Bethel Chapel Heathfield Road, Liverpool 15 on 10 June 1996 and afterwards in Springwood Crematorium. His ashes were dispersed by St Tudno's Church on the Gogarth Llandudno. A Robert Arthur

Hughes Memorial Lecture was arranged by the North East India-Wales Trust in Liverpool between 1997 and 2007 and six were arranged. The first three lectures were enlarged and published in a volume under the title The Call and Contribution of Dr Robert Arthur Hughes OBE, FRCS 1910-1996 and some of his predecessors in North East India (Liverpool 2004).

D Andrew Jones, 'The Mission Understanding of Dr Arthur Hughes' [in] The Call and Contribution of Dr Robert Arthur Hughes OBE, FRCS 1910-1996 and some of his predecessors in North East India (Liverpool 2004), 42-72; D. Ben Rees, 'The Doctor with a Mission', The Guardian (14 June 1996); D. Ben Rees, 'The Life and Work of Dr R Arthur Hughes, OBE, FRCS', [in] The Call and Contribution of Dr Robert Arthur Hughes, OBE, FRCS 190-1996 and some of his predecessors in North East India (Liverpool, 2004), 11-38; D. Ben Rees, 'Robert Arthur Hughes OBE, FRCS', 75th Anniversary, 1922-1997, Their Vision, Our Legacy. The KJP Synod Hospital, Shillong, formerly known as the Khasi Hills Welsh Mission Hospital (Shillong, 1997), 51-55.